CU00919221

BRIGHTER

Optimism, Progress, and the
Future of Environmentalism

ADAM DORR

Rethink X

RethinkX
rethinkx.com

Copyright © 2023 Adam Dorr
All rights reserved.
adamdorr.com

Image in Figure 13: © Steve Gschmeissner, 2016, reproduced with permission.

Cover art, design, and illustrations by Adam Dorr

LIBRARY OF CONGRESS CATALOGING-IN-PUBLICATION DATA
Names: Dorr, Adam, 1976- author.
Title: Brighter : Optimism, Progress, and the Future of the Environment /
Adam Dorr.

Description: 1st Edition. p. cm. | San Francisco : RethinkX, 2023. |
Includes bibliographic references and index.

ISBN 979-8-9872530-0-7 (hardcover)
ISBN 979-8-9872530-1-4 (paperback)
ISBN 979-8-9872530-2-1 (eBook)
ISBN 979-8-9872530-4-5 (international edition)

Subjects: 1. Progress. 2. Environmentalism. 3. Technological innovations--
Forecasting. | Classification: LCC T173.2-174.5

Printed in the United States of America

For Misora and Kaiyomi

ACKNOWLEDGEMENTS

Thank you to Tony Seba and James Arbib. This book would not have been possible without your extraordinary generosity, compassion, and support. You have been unwavering beacons of light and hope during a time of unimaginable darkness and despair.

Thank you to my colleagues at RethinkX. The extraordinary work we have done is a testament to the talent and tenacity of each and every one of you who I have had the privilege of calling my teammates over the last five years.

Thank you to my family and friends. Your love and patience have been an invaluable source of inspiration and strength.

And thank you to Stephanie, for absolutely everything. Our journey together is only just beginning.

CONTENTS

INTRODUCTION

"Optimism doesn't mean that you are blind to the reality of the situation. It means that you remain motivated to seek a solution to whatever problems arise."

– His Holiness the 14th Dalai Lama

There has never been greater cause for optimism about the future of the environment.

This is not a personal opinion or an empty platitude. It is an incontrovertible fact. But very few people are aware of this fact and the growing mountain of evidence that supports it.

I have written this book because everywhere I look, I see my family and friends and fellow environmentalists despairing about our prospects for meeting the formidable environmental challenges we face and healing our wounded world. Even my colleagues in the environmental science, policy, and planning disciplines are unaware of how bright the future truly is.

This book is for everyone, but most especially for those who are pessimistic about the future. It is for the public, to give a clearer view of the road ahead and provide a rational basis for optimism. It is for environmental activists and advocates, to help them better understand technology and the outsized role it will play in enabling us to meet our goals. It is for decisionmakers, to help them focus on the right policies, investments, and initiatives, and avoid wasting resources on the wrong ones. And it is for my fellow scholars and scientists, to help reframe the substantive content and future research of our disciplines within the context of disruptive technological change.

Environmental problems are very real and they are extremely serious.

Climate change and ocean acidification, biodiversity loss and species extinction, overfishing and coral bleaching, deforestation and desertification, habitat fragmentation and destruction, air and water pollution, soil contamination and erosion, factory farming and animal rights – all of these issues and more threaten ecological integrity and human wellbeing, and none of them can be ignored. To the contrary, the state of some of these problems – especially climate change – is even worse than the public generally believes, because most scientists are only willing to stake their reputations on the most conservative scenarios, not the scenarios that they privately believe the evidence indicates are most realistic.

But our current situation is not hopeless, because we are not helpless. Although the present moment is a critical juncture in many respects, what lies ahead is not a brick wall we must retreat from but rather a chasm we must build a bridge across.

Why now?

Over the next two decades we will witness the most comprehensive technological transformation of the global economy in over a century. Four foundational sectors will be disrupted: energy, transportation, food, and labor. Each of these disruptions by itself would be world-changing, just as the recent disruption of the information sector by the Internet was world-changing. But all four together simultaneously is nothing short of astonishing. And we are extremely fortunate that all four of these disruptions will be *clean*. This didn't have to be the case, as we have had many dirty technology disruptions in the past – perhaps most famously when fossil fuels disrupted biofuels like wood and whale oil, and when the combustion engines they powered disrupted horses and oxen.

Disruption is different than slow, incremental technological progress. Disruption happens when new technology emerges that dramatically outperforms and out-competes older technology, which rapidly transforms a market, industry, or entire sector of the economy as a result. History shows us that disruptions are not linear. They always follow an s-curve, starting off slowly, before exploding exponentially, and then eventually slowing down again as they reach saturation. As the new technologies grow, they wipe out the older ones that can no longer compete. Because they are nonlinear, disruptions tend to sneak up on us, and then suddenly they unfold much, much faster than we expect – within just a decade or two. For things as different as cameras are from car tires, as different as carpenter's nails are from insulin, we see the same pattern of disruption again and again throughout history. For example, we used horses for transportation for thousands of years, but a century ago they were disrupted by cars in just 15 years. Similarly, Kodak was the titan of photography for over a century, but then the first affordable consumer digital cameras came out in 1995 and by 2010 Kodak was bankrupt and most of us couldn't remember the last time we'd bought a roll of film.

Disruptions also do more than just swap a new technology for an old one. Electricity wasn't just cheaper whale oil, automobiles weren't just faster horses, and farming wasn't just more fruitful hunting and gathering. These technologies transformed energy, transportation, and food – and civilization along with them. And now it's about to happen again.

In energy, the technologies are solar power, wind power, and batteries. A decade ago, they were still expensive. Now they are cheap, and getting cheaper by the minute. By 2030 they will be overwhelmingly competitive everywhere, which is why they are growing exponentially worldwide. The change to our energy system will be profound because energy goes into virtually everything else we make and do, and so the impacts of this disruption will reverberate through every corner of the global economy, making *everything* cheaper and cleaner.

In transportation, the technologies are electric vehicles, autonomous driving, and ride-hailing. They are cheap and getting cheaper, and growing exponentially too. Electric, autonomous cars and trucks powered by sunlight and wind that don't need expensive fuel or a driver will move people and goods at a fraction of the cost of road transport today – and without emissions that cause air pollution or climate change. Like energy, the impacts of this disruption will reverberate through every corner of the global economy.

In food, the technologies are precision fermentation (which makes proteins and other molecules with microbes), and cellular agriculture (which makes meat from animal cells, without the animal). The first commercial products are now available, and a decade from now we will be eating 'animal' products that aren't made from animals at all. Moreover, these new forms of meat, dairy, and seafood will be superior in every way – tastier, healthier, safer, and much cheaper. Compared to animal products, these technologies are 10 times more water efficient, 20 times more time efficient, and up to 100 times more land efficient, and so it's no surprise that they are growing exponentially too. The change to our food system will be shocking. The collapse of animal farming will free up over 2.5 billion hectares – an area of land the size of the United States, China, and Australia *combined*. The unprecedented opportunities for reforestation, conservation, and rewilding will be staggering. The change in the oceans will be stunning as well, because many marine ecosystems can recover quite quickly once we are no longer strip-mining them with millions of commercial fishing vessels.

In labor, the technologies are machine learning and artificial intelligence, which open the door to genuinely sophisticated automation. This will enable machines to perform complex tasks like driving that today can only be done by human beings. We are only just now reaching the point where computers and software can give 'robots' enough brainpower to navigate within complex, dynamic three-dimensional environments and interact adaptively with other objects and agents in the physical world. But a machine that can learn to drive in Los Angeles or Shanghai can also learn to operate in a warehouse, a factory floor, a supermarket, a kitchen, and thousands of other workplaces, and so self-driving vehicles are the pebble that will trigger the automation avalanche. The implications of disrupting human labor are profound, and while machine labor has the potential to free us from the perennial shackles of drudgery and turbocharge productivity like nothing the world has ever seen, it also has the potential to plunge society into chaos. In a world with little demand for human labor, we will need to fundamentally rethink human rights, and relinquish the belief that every person must 'earn their keep' through toil unless they are lucky enough to already own a large amount of rentable property or interest-generating capital.

Why be optimistic?

Our current environmental trajectory is unsustainable, and concern is not just reasonable but obligatory. But the future of the environment is very much brighter than most of us think, because very nearly all environmental problems are solvable with the right tools. And the imminent disruption of energy, transportation, food, and labor means that we are much closer to having those tools in hand than most of us imagine.

The bulk of this book is devoted to explaining why genuine solutions to our most pressing environmental problems are attainable in the near term with technology, and how this justifies optimism about the future of the environment. My hope is that this will help serve as an antidote not only to the pessimism but also the false hope and magical thinking that pervade contemporary environmentalism. This book is not about mustering an optimistic *attitude*, it is about having *reasons* for being optimistic. Having a clear view of our technological future is in turn crucial to making sound environmental policy, planning, advocacy, and investment decisions going forward.

However, technology is going to do far more than just help us solve the environmental problems we face today. It is going to fundamentally transform our relationship with the natural world from one of dependency to one of stewardship. This transformation has profound implications for the future of nature, and so the book closes by challenging us to rethink environmentalism for the 21st Century based not on who we are today as individuals and as a civilization, but on who we aspire to become.

Why listen?

I am fortunate to be in a position of extraordinary privilege that is very unusual for a scientist, because I am *not* beholden to grantmakers, tenure review boards, university deans or provosts or presidents, journal editors, publishers, or paying clients. This means that I am free to be completely candid where many of my colleagues are less able to challenge established orthodoxies. In fact, challenging orthodoxies is what I do: I am currently the Director of Research for an independent think tank supported philanthropically with zero strings attached, and so I have absolute freedom to call things exactly as I see them. Like many think tanks, RethinkX has a specific lens – in our case, the lens of technological disruption – through which it selects and analyzes topics of interest. But unlike many others, this lens is neither political nor ideological. It is pragmatic, not dogmatic. Our methodology is just as likely to conclude a technology is a dead end (e.g. hydrogen-powered cars) as it is to conclude that a technology will be disruptive (e.g. battery electric vehicles). My 'agenda' is simple, transparent, and unequivocal: to be as honest and well-informed as possible about how to maximize human and ecological flourishing as technology continues to advance.

The content of this book might therefore be confusing to some readers because it does not conform to any orthodoxy. My hope, however, is that this will challenge readers to assess the substance of the book on its own merits rather than paint it with the broad brush of any conventional ideological affiliation. To that end, I also hope that this book comes as a breath of fresh air, with new information and reasoning about the future of the natural world and environmentalism that gives readers something genuinely exciting to think about.

Above all, I hope readers will find both my deep concern about the environment and my abiding optimism in human progress compelling enough to be contagious. Our future is far, *far* brighter than many of us dare to imagine.

CHAPTER 1

PROBLEMS, PROSPERITY, AND PROGRESS

"Stars are phoenixes, rising from their own ashes."

– Carl Sagan

Your house is on fire. What should you do?

First, put the fire out. That part is obvious. It's also obvious that you need to put out *all* of the fire. Extinguishing only *some* of the flames isn't going to solve your problem. To do so, you need the right tools because fighting the fire alone with a bucket won't get the job done. You need to call the Fire Department so they can deploy the equipment this emergency demands.

Second, and perhaps less obvious while you're staring at the blaze, is that you will also need to repair and upgrade your house. You're not done when the fire is out – not even close. Extinguishing the flames is the easy part. You're only done when you've fixed all the damage, rebuilt what was ruined, and added safeguards to prevent future fires from occurring. And you're not going to get that done alone with a bucket either. You'll need to call in a variety of different experts, each with specialized tools for their part of the job.

Now, consider climate change: *our world* is on fire, and the conventional narrative about how to deal with this crisis isn't just wrong, it's ludicrous. We cannot solve climate change by consuming *less* and reducing *some* of our greenhouse gas emissions, any more than we can save a burning building by putting out *some* of the fire. And getting to net zero emissions, like putting out a fire, is only the first half of the job. Once there, we will still have a huge amount of repair and restoration work ahead of us because the planet won't magically heal overnight by itself from the damage we've already done over the last several centuries.

So, the bad news is that climate change is a much bigger problem than most of us imagine. We cannot solve this crisis by taking shorter showers, driving a bit less, and not eating meat on Mondays. The situation is much too serious for that now. The same is true for many other environmental problems beyond just climate change as well. We need far more powerful tools to meet these formidable challenges. The good news, however, is that we already have those tools. They are the clean technologies that will completely transform energy, transportation, food, and labor over the next 20 years – and civilization along with them.

Dangerous doomsaying

If we really were doomed by climate change, then it would logically follow that all other human progress has been for nothing. Everything our civilization has achieved – every disease we've ever cured, every peace we've ever forged, every scientific discovery we've ever made, every step toward wisdom and enlightenment we've ever taken – fire, the wheel, language, music, writing, art, philosophy – all of it has been for naught if we wipe ourselves out with climate change.

Thankfully, the idea that we are doomed by climate change is dead wrong. But the fatalism and nihilism arising from this false belief have begun to infect an entire generation worldwide.

At the individual level, despair over climate change and the false belief that our future is unavoidably bleak has cast a long shadow across countless lives. Eco-anxiety is a growing mental health problem worldwide, and recent research has shown that more than half of young adults globally are so worried about climate change that it negatively impacts their daily lives and plans for the future.[1] I have personally had colleagues, friends, neighbors, and family members confess reluctance to have children for fear of the dystopian world they believe lies ahead of us, and it breaks my heart every time.

At the societal level, the false belief that human prosperity is the *cause* of climate change but not also the *solution* to it has threatened to poison the well of progress itself. This backwards thinking is not just a dispiriting irony. It is a genuinely dangerous idea that could have disastrous consequences if taken too seriously for too long, because it undermines our collective capacity to actually solve the problems we face.

What are problems, anyway?

When we see the world is one way, and we wish it were another, we call that situation a problem. And the way we solve problems is by transforming the world from a less desirable state into a more desirable state. This is equally true both for the world outside of us and the world within ourselves.

As I write this section of the book, it's winter here in Michigan. "Hey Dad," my daughter Misora said to me a few days ago, "can you help me with my coat?" The heavy brass zipper was getting stuck at the bottom, and after trying for a minute or two I realized it was bent out of shape and I just didn't have the finger strength to fix it by hand. So I grabbed a pair of pliers out of the kitchen junk drawer and gave it a few careful pinches. "There you go, good as new!" I said, as it slid freely once again. In a blink, she was off out the door, calling out "thanks Dad!" over her shoulder as she ran to catch up with her friends.

In that small but satisfying moment of fixing a broken zipper, I marveled at the great chain of human ingenuity across the centuries that made it possible: millions of people with countless ideas solving problems of every describable kind – materials, design, manufacturing, logistics, and more. Zippers solve the problem of how to join two edges of cloth. Pliers solve the problem of how to grip things with superhuman strength. Winter coats solve the problem of how to stay warm and dry in conditions that would otherwise quickly prove lethal. Take a moment to consider the chain of ingenuity behind the simple, everyday objects within reach around you at this moment: they are all tools of a sort, because they represent the embodied practical knowledge of how to solve problems by transforming the world in desirable ways. The same is also true of all the much larger things around which we organize our lives, like buildings and roads and farms and airports. And it is true for many of the less tangible things that shape our lives as well, from energy and mobility to institutions and laws.

Our capacity to solve problems is thus directly determined by our capacity to undertake transformations of the world around us. So, what exactly is it that determines this capacity?

Many different answers to that question could be given at various levels of analysis, but if we were to distill them all into a single word, it would be: *prosperity*.

Prosperity is the term we use to describe the general condition in which we possess sufficient means *and* know-how to transform our world or ourselves in needed ways. And the greater the problem we face, the more prosperity we require to solve it.

Now, to be clear, money and other forms of capital are not the same thing as prosperity, they are only part of the picture. Wealth alone is not enough to solve problems – it is often a necessary condition, but seldom a sufficient condition in itself. Moreover, prosperity (of a sort) is possible even without money or other forms of material wealth, and a person can become more prosperous by leveraging knowledge alone to change their personal mindset and outlook. But no matter how 'prosperous' our ancestors thousands of years ago might have been, their capacity to solve problems was severely limited compared to ours by any reasonable measure. This doesn't mean that they didn't *try* to solve their problems, however. Though their efforts were futile, they made perfectly heroic attempts to meet the challenges they faced. But their approaches often focused on making ritual sacrifices, signaling piousness and virtue, and attempting to atone for sins in order to appease gods, ancestors, and other imagined authorities. If this sounds eerily familiar, it should, because this is exactly what we are doing now in response to climate change, and it is precisely the sort of desperate action we would expect to see from any society that lacks the means and know-how to actually solve its problems effectively.

As prosperous as our societies are today, there of course remain problems we cannot yet solve – climate change being chief among them. But this does not mean that *no* amount of prosperity could solve them. A century from now, amidst a degree of prosperity we can scarcely imagine today, our descendants will look back upon our struggle to solve climate change the same way we look back at our ancestors' struggle to secure food and shelter.

At some level, this entire line of reasoning should be intuitively obvious. After all, we depend on our own individual prosperity to solve problems in our personal lives every day. Why should it be any different for entire societies?

The path to despair

A major theme in conventional environmental discourse is that humanity has made a Faustian bargain, and that the prosperity we enjoy today has been bought at a terrible price whose bill has finally come due. Our only option now, so the narrative goes, is to give up prosperity and embrace austerity instead – cut back, tighten our belts, consume less. And the greater our level of personal or collective prosperity is today, the further we must descend to reach sustainability. It is no accident that there is a strong moralizing element to this narrative, because it explicitly and unapologetically asserts that we must sacrifice our quality of life going forward to atone for the sins of our past indulgences. And the most prosperous individuals and nations, whose sins are greatest, must be punished most.

But in my experience, most people intuitively understand that we cannot *really* hope to solve major challenges like climate change this way. The train of thought goes something like this:

> *Our common sense screams at us that solving problems*
> *takes prosperity, and so if we really, truly cannot solve climate*
> *change with prosperity as the conventional narrative goes, then*

we don't stand a snowball's chance in hell of solving climate change without it. Then, when we hear authorities of various stripes proclaiming that the solution is just to think optimistically and embrace austerity with a plucky attitude, it sets off our bullshit detector like a fire alarm. It all has the ring of desperation to it, because we would never even consider the nonsense of trading one disaster for another if a real solution were available.

OK, but then what if climate change really is in fact an unsolvable problem, and the authorities are just too afraid to admit it openly? Well, we will all just have to learn to live with it, won't we? But wait… if climate change is indeed the catastrophic existential risk that the scientific community says it is, then there won't be any "learning to live with it", will there? It's a no-win scenario. We're all just toast.

I believe this line of thinking is one of the root causes of why so many people have been driven to despair. Who wouldn't be discouraged, given such a dismal view of the future?

Doom and gloom are dead wrong

Thankfully, this conventional view is dead wrong. My team's research along with a growing body of work by other scientists worldwide has shown that climate change is a solvable problem, and that prosperity is of course the solution – just as it has been for virtually every other problem in human experience. The disruption of energy, transportation, food, and labor will slash costs across these sectors by up to 90% and trigger an explosion of prosperity, especially in poorer countries, while simultaneously mitigating virtually all greenhouse gas emissions – and not by the end of the century, but by the 2040s.[2]

I have been overwhelmed by the positive response to our research about these disruptions and their implications for climate change. People not only find our work fascinating and uplifting, but perhaps more importantly they find it *convincing*. Very tellingly, it comes as a relief to them after the cognitive dissonance they have felt from the conventional narrative. Our findings naturally align with what most people already know in their bones to be true about the need for prosperity to solve big problems. Furthermore, because our findings aren't full of logical contradictions or ideological moralizing, they don't set off the usual alarm bells that we all experience when someone is trying to sell us on something bogus.

The road to hell is once again paved with good intentions

My fellow environmental scientists – and the policymakers, planners, and activists that depend on their research – are not deliberately misleading us. There is no grand conspiracy, no intentional deception, no malice here. There is only error: a series of mistakes and false assumptions, rooted in a failure to understand the history and dynamics of disruptive technological change, that have compounded one upon the other to result in the terribly misguided prescription that humanity ought to respond to climate change with a regress into austerity. Like medieval doctors prescribing bloodletting out of ignorance and desperation, it won't work, it will only make things worse.

At some level, the public already knows this. After all, our common sense tells us that when something we're doing is creating a problem, the solution usually isn't just to do *less* of that thing and hope for the best, but to stop and do something different altogether. As we saw at the beginning of the chapter, if your house is on fire you need to do much more than put out *some* of the flames. The same is true for climate change. The solution isn't *less* energy, transportation, and food, which together account for almost 90% of global greenhouse gas emissions. The solution is *clean* energy, transportation, and food to stop making the problem worse, and then a massive undertaking of carbon withdrawal to repair the damage we've already done up until now.

The good news is that we already have the clean technologies we need, and the disruption of these three foundational sectors of the global economy is now inevitable. But with the clock ticking on climate change, we must still make the right choices – as individuals, as industries, as nations – to accelerate rather than delay these disruptions. We can do so with our voices, with our votes, and with our wallets. The sooner we do, the sooner we can meet this formidable challenge.

The trouble with climate change is that the incumbent authorities to which the public looks for guidance, including most especially the scientific community, have so far failed to provide a coherent and compelling plan for how humanity can correct course. This has understandably led to confusion and despair, because being told that the way to meet the enormous challenge of climate change is with personal sacrifice, lifestyle change, and other forms of individual austerity rather than with collective prosperity – in direct contradiction of virtually all other historical examples of problem solving – rings false on many levels. What it really feels like is that the scientific community thinks the situation is hopeless but is refusing to admit it to us. Sadly, I can personally attest that this is indeed precisely what a good number of my colleagues in the environmental disciplines have privately believed for the last decade or more.

The real issue, of course, is that significant blocs of the scientific community have failed to understand precisely *how* prosperity can solve climate change. Filling this gap in our knowledge is an important part of the work that my research team has done over the last several years. The answer is via the clean disruption of energy, transportation, food, and labor. Moreover, the prosperity these disruptions generate will in turn enable us to solve many other environmental and social problems as well.

Problems are inevitable

Problems are inevitable, whether naturally occurring or of our own making. The only thing that stands between us and the next civilization-ending threat is how much problem-solving capacity – meaning how much *prosperity* – we develop between now and then. That means progress is our only real protection from disaster, whether we like it or not – including from problems we have inadvertently created ourselves. To lose sight of this puts us in very grave peril, and the reason why deserves the strongest possible emphasis:

Every society at every moment in human history has always been just one unsolvable problem away from annihilation, and we are no exception.

Every past society that ever collapsed – and there have been many throughout the ages – did so because it faced a challenge it could not overcome. There is debate among scientists, for example, about the cause of the catastrophic deforestation and ecological collapse that occurred on Rapa Nui, or Easter Island, some time prior to the 19th Century. Did the indigenous society shortsightedly overexploit and mismanage the island's finite natural resources? Or were the inhabitants wise resource managers whose forests collapsed because of damage caused by rats and other invasive species? Or was sustainable utilization of Rapa Nui's natural resources the norm up until the arrival of colonial Europeans whose diseases ravaged the local population and plunged their society into chaos and war?

Whatever the true answer may be, these scenarios all miss the much more fundamental point that *the society on Rapa Nui failed to solve the problems it faced*. No matter how 'sustainable' that society might have been, it failed to sustain its people when they needed it most: in the face of enormous unanticipated problems. What *would* have helped them overcome these problems is better tools, more knowledge, and greater prosperity. These are things which can only be obtained by making progress.

Dozens of human societies throughout history, and 99.9% of all species that have ever lived including all of our close hominid cousins, were wiped out because they lacked the means to solve the problems they faced. We are safer today, yes, but not yet safe enough to be complacent. If an asteroid impact of the kind that wiped out the dinosaurs struck the Earth tomorrow, it would almost surely be the end of us as well. But, thanks to progress, we are now prosperous enough to have a fighting chance of detecting and deflecting the next world-upending asteroid or other existential threat before it is too late – and that includes climate change.

Consider the COVID-19 pandemic. As imperfect as our response was, one aspect of it that brooks absolutely no criticism is the astounding speed with which we were able to develop effective vaccines. But what if, in the name of avoiding climate change, we had only allowed half as much economic growth and technological progress over the last 100 years instead? How many years would vaccine development have taken with 1970s technology? And how many more would have died as a result? Now, imagine our situation if the virus had been ten times as lethal and had primarily struck children instead of the elderly. Such viruses do arise – indeed, it is almost inevitable that our luck will run out and we will face one of that kind sooner or later.

True, we would have reduced greenhouse gas emissions by 50% in this imaginary scenario. But, having made only half as much technological progress since the 1920s, we would also now have to wait another century until the 2120s before clean technologies were finally ready to disrupt energy, transportation, and food and take us to net zero emissions and beyond. So instead of starting to decarbonize in the 2020s as we are today, in this scenario we would be stuck spending the next 100 years continuing to emit carbon anyway. Would that really have been a more sustainable outcome?

The idea of *regress*, however, can be seductive. We are inundated by news media, film, television, literature, and advertising with claims that the past and the primitive offer valid guides for how to live sustainably. But with few exceptions, this is a childish and dangerously irresponsible fantasy that we ought not to indulge.

What is progress?

We all aspire to help build a brighter future – for ourselves, for our family and friends, for our planet. But what does that actually mean? Is progress something we can even define, given that not everyone shares the same preferences? People with different cultural backgrounds and religious or political beliefs have historically disagreed so strongly with one another about how the world ought to be that they have gone to war and committed unthinkable atrocities in the name of 'progress'. How can we move forward if we cannot agree where we ought to be headed?

The concept of progress has long been a contentious topic among scholars, and even seemingly unobjectionable definitions, such as "an increase in human flourishing measured by life, health, sustenance, prosperity, peace, freedom, safety, knowledge, leisure, and happiness visible in data," are hotly debated and criticized.[3] When I was teaching at UCLA, I would ask my students how they thought humanity should deal with the dilemma of how to define progress and a brighter future, and although there were spirited arguments about the merits of different moral, philosophical, and aesthetic sensibilities, the discussion would always settle on the same compromise: *progress ought to maximize freedom of choice.*

A brighter future is not one in which we limit our options, but one in which we expand them. A brighter future is not about conforming to any single vision, but about creating a plethora of possibilities and ensuring that everyone everywhere has the freedom and the means to explore whichever ones they choose.

We all instinctively know this. Creating options for ourselves and accruing the means to pursue our interests and values is the reason why we work hard and try to get ahead, why we hope to strike it rich or win the lottery, and why we seek social status and influence. The real value of wealth and power is that they buy us more choices.

Our challenge is not to build a world where everyone is wealthy and powerful – that is a fool's errand because of the relative nature of those measures. Instead, our challenge is to build a world of such abundance that freedom of choice is overwhelmingly available to all people worldwide regardless of status, and where human prosperity does not come at an unsustainable cost to the natural world.

The only way to meet this challenge and build a brighter future is with better technology.

Degrowth versus decoupling

Environmental problems like climate change are the result of unintended consequences. Yes, humanity has been reckless and selfish and shortsighted. But we are not malicious. Most of us are not diabolical comic book villains who take delight in watching the world burn. The harm we are doing to the planet is *not* deliberate, and this fact has profound implications because problems caused by accident are much easier to solve than problems caused on purpose.

We can extend the earlier analogy of a house on fire to illustrate how important the differences are between accidental and deliberate harm. In the accidental version, imagine we are heating our house with soggy green wood in an old fireplace. There is no fire screen for protection, so sparks keep flying out into the living room and setting things on fire. In the deliberate version, however, imagine there is an arsonist with a vendetta against our family who is determined to burn our house down, and who will therefore adapt to any efforts we make to put the fire out or prevent it from starting in the first place. One situation is obviously much, *much* worse than the other. In both cases the fire is equally harmful and equally predictable, but our options for how we can solve the problem in each case are completely different.

It is obvious which of these two situations we are in. Karma and fate are not out to punish us. Climate change and other environmental problems are simply an unintended side effect of using imperfect tools, and we can solve them by developing and using better tools – just as we have done so many times in the past. Cholera and typhoid, for example, weren't the curses of angry gods or karmic justice for our sins, they were just a sanitation problem. We solved that problem with hygiene, plumbing, and chlorinated water, and we will solve all other environmental problems the same way: through ingenuity, innovation, and progress.

The house on fire analogy offers us insight into one of the most fundamental environmental debates, which is the *degrowth* approach versus the *decoupling* approach to solving climate change and other environmental problems.

Degrowth is a school of thought centered on the idea that the best way to reduce environmental impact is simply to do less of the things that result in harm. The degrowth orthodoxy argues that because we cannot fully meet humans needs with the tools available today without causing unsustainable environmental damage to the planet, we must learn to live with less. Importantly, this orthodoxy also asserts that we can improve quality of life for most of the world's people (to a modest extent) by focusing on eliminating disparities of wealth, income, and other advantages.[4-6]

Decoupling, by contrast, is a school of thought centered on the idea that we can find ways to fully meet human needs with less and less environmental impact through new technology and other forms of innovation. Although the economic activities that meet human needs today are indeed coupled with unavoidable side effects, this school of thought holds that there is no reason to believe we will be stuck with primitive tools forever. Rather, we can continue to make progress and eventually reduce our ecological footprint to a negligible level.[7–9]

Degrowth is a can't-do worldview, whereas decoupling is a can-do worldview. The degrowth orthodoxy casts a wide net of blame across our entire modern way of life – on capitalism and markets, on government corruption, on corporate greed, on consumerism, on personal lifestyle choices – and perhaps with good reason. But it offers little of practical value beyond the obvious (be less wasteful), the naïve (abolish capitalism), or the sanctimonious (be contented with less). Moreover, the degrowth orthodoxy justifies its conclusions as much on moral as on rational grounds: those individuals and societies that have enjoyed the highest quality of life in the past must give up their indulgent luxuries like air travel and single-family homes in the name of fairness and justice; equitability must be achieved punitively by dragging the undeserving 'rich' or 'the 1%' downward, not merely by elevating the less fortunate upward. This is not to say that gross socioeconomic disparities are acceptable – they absolutely are not, and no decent or sane person would claim otherwise. But as romantically appealing as a Robinhood approach might be, it's just not practically realistic. The Norwegian psychologist, economist, and Green Party parliament member Per Esper Stoknes has likened it to thinking that, "if we bake a smaller cake, then for some reason the poorest will get a bigger share of it," which has "never happened in history".[10]

Would it be better if we could somehow convince or even force every society to be as egalitarian as Norway? Perhaps. But a perfectly egalitarian global GDP per capita would be $12,500 per year.[i] Given how large humanity's ecological footprint is now, that figure would still need to 'degrow' by at least 80% for us to even begin approaching sustainability with today's dirty technologies. An 'equitable' and 'sustainable' future where everyone subsists on an amount of material consumption equivalent to $2,500 per year is simply not good enough. Our children and grandchildren deserve better than that.

Moreover, the degrowth narrative often conflates intended and unintended consequences, which is a category mistake and fundamental logical error. Growth is not itself inherently good or bad. Rather, it is the specific consequences of growth which matter. It is unequivocally true that economic growth has been instrumental in increasing material prosperity through technological progress, which in turn has helped us live safer, healthier, freer, fairer, longer, and more fulfilling lives.[11] But it is equally true that this has increased humanity's ecological footprint to an unsustainable level, as every environmental scientist and activist knows so well. Growth itself therefore deserves no credit or blame either way. It is the specific consequences that deserve our attention. Energy isn't bad, *greenhouse gas emissions* are bad. Transportation isn't bad, *air pollution and traffic* are bad. High-protein foods aren't bad, *mistreating animals and deforesting land for livestock* is bad. The presumption of the degrowth orthodoxy that the benefits of growth are inescapably coupled to the harmful side effects is false.

The decoupling approach therefore does not blame people or institutions or economic growth at large for our environmental problems, any more than it would have blamed angry gods or fate for cholera and typhoid. Instead, it more correctly attributes our failure to thus far solve environmental problems to the limited tools we currently have to work with. The way to solve these problems is not to 'degrow' our global economy, but to decouple its benefits from its harms by continuing to make technological progress.

Problems are solvable

Every problem posing an existential threat that we have ever faced has had a solution, or else humanity wouldn't be here. Although truly unsolvable problems are conceivable, such as a cataclysmic astronomical event that devastates our entire solar system, these are so vanishingly rare that we can ignore them. Every problem we are ever likely to face, including the proverbial dinosaur-killing comet or asteroid, will be something that we can solve *if* we have the right tools and knowledge along with sufficient prosperity to utilize them quickly and effectively enough to avert catastrophe. Climate change is no exception.

We are not monsters. We are a technological species whose environmental problems are an unintended side effect of using tools that are less than perfect. But "use tools less" is neither a rational nor a practical solution, so we are left with only one rational choice: *use better tools*.

The term *tools* is of course synonymous with technology in this context, and from the simple maxim of *use better tools* follows a general 3-step recipe for successful environmental problem-solving:

1. Develop better technology and switch to it when it becomes economically competitive.
2. Use that technology to reduce ongoing environmental damage.
3. Use that technology to repair past environmental damage.

For Step 1, it is possible to accelerate both the development and the adoption of better, cleaner technologies with social choices. We can choose to kickstart research and development through public institutions like universities and government laboratories (and even crowd-sourcing), rather than relying solely on private innovation. Then, once viable commercial products emerge, we can choose to incentivize adoption and deployment in the early days when they are still expensive by subsidizing the new technologies and/or penalizing the older ones with regulatory interventions. However, a new technology must have the potential to eventually stand on its own merits and become economically competitive without assistance in order for its market dominance to be assured.

For Step 2, adoption of the new technology displaces the older technology, thereby eliminating ongoing environmental damage at its source. In environmental jargon, this is known as *mitigation*, and perhaps the most familiar example is the replacement of fossil fuels by renewables like solar and wind power, which reduces greenhouse gas emissions. To invoke a medical analogy, mitigation means *stop doing harm*.

For Step 3, adoption of the new technology allows us to repair the damage we've already done to the environment, either directly by utilizing the new tools themselves, or indirectly by making repair efforts more affordable. In environmental jargon, this is known as *ecological restoration* or simply *restoration*.[ii] For example, we could use clean energy from solar and wind power to run machines that capture carbon dioxide directly from the air, helping to repair the damage our past greenhouse gas emissions have done to the atmosphere and oceans. Alternatively, we could use the cheap clean energy they generate to indirectly make the entire reforestation supply chain more affordable, and then engage in more reforestation to capture carbon dioxide in the biomass of trees, thus repairing the damage from past emissions that way. To continue the medical analogy, restoration means *healing*.

In simpler terms, the recipe for success is: *innovation, mitigation*, and *restoration*.

This basic 3-step process applies to *all* environmental problems, not just climate change, so it is a useful way to organize our thinking and focus our efforts. In the chapters ahead we will apply the 3-step approach above and explore the details for each of the major types of environmental problems we face.

Solving problems is hard

Simple doesn't necessarily mean easy, as anyone who has ever gone to the gym knows. Even though better tools borne of progress and prosperity are the best solution available for our most daunting environmental problems, implementing them will still be difficult and painful in many ways. The livelihoods and traditions of millions of people that are tied to old industries will be disrupted by new technologies, as they have been many times before throughout history, and we must be prepared long in advance to protect and support those who are negatively affected. It is crucial that individuals, communities, and entire societies anticipate disruption and build the capacity to adapt ahead of time. We need to *get ready* for what's coming, and soon.

Moreover, there won't be a single one-size-fits-all approach that works in every location, given the enormous cultural and geographic variation across the globe, and so the process of getting ready will look different from one community and society to another. We need to begin experimenting now to find out what works and what doesn't, and learn from one another's successes and failures as quickly as possible. Denying and resisting the disruptions, or even just procrastinating, will only invite chaos and suffering once the flood of change arrives.

The overwhelming reason why we fail to solve environmental problems today is not for lack of knowledge or lack of concern, but for lack of prosperity. For example, a substantial fraction of the plastic pollution in the world's oceans originates from a small number of rivers in poorer countries.[12] Those rivers are not full of trash because the people who live near them don't know or don't care about polluting the environment. They are no different than you or me, and it would be arrogant and bigoted to believe otherwise. Rather, those rivers are full of trash because the nearby communities are simply too impoverished to afford the expensive waste management systems we environmentalists in the wealthiest countries take for granted. And that means the solution to trash in those rivers is not education or advocacy. Those communities don't need to be lectured. They need *more prosperity*, and the best way to achieve that is by making progress.

We already have the tools we need to solve climate change

In RethinkX's 2021 research report, *Rethinking Climate Change*, we explained that the disruption of energy (by solar power, wind power, and batteries), transportation (by electric vehicles, autonomous driving, and ride hailing), and food (by precision fermentation and cellular agriculture) will allow us to reduce net emissions 90% by 2035, on track to going far below zero into a deep carbon withdrawal regime in the 2040s. This solution to climate change, which we will explore in depth in Chapter 4, directly reflects the 3-step recipe for success above.

An additional crucial finding of our research, however, is that the technologies that we need to solve climate change already exist. They are science fact today, not science fiction.

That means we don't need to waste time and resources on numerous band-aid fixes like 'clean coal', 'clean diesel', or feeding cows seaweed and teaching them to use toilets in hopes that we can chip away enough of the emissions problem to make a meaningful difference before it is too late. Instead, we can tackle climate change head-on using the same thing that has worked every time for every other major challenge in human experience: better tools and knowledge borne of progress and prosperity.

Justifiable optimism

Perhaps the most compelling aspect of my team's research is that it shows there is now good *reason* to be optimistic about solving climate change and other serious environmental problems. This is an entirely different kind of optimism from the sanctimony of the conventional environmental narratives that merely urge us to adopt an optimistic *attitude* as a way to cope with what otherwise appears to be a no-win situation.

It has been a joy and a privilege to watch people come to understand that there is a legitimate, evidence-based pathway to solving climate change and other major environmental problems, because they experience a sudden relief from all of the confusion and despair caused by the conventional narratives. Being the bearer of this good news is like giving water to a person dying of thirst. It has changed my life. Not long ago, for example, a gentleman named William approached me after a presentation with tears in his eyes. He explained that he and his wife had decided not to have children because of the bleak future they believed lay ahead, but that after learning from our work that there is genuine cause for optimism, he had changed his mind. I have no words to describe the beauty of that moment.

Restoring our faith in human progress

The despair caused by the false belief that climate change is an unsolvable problem has eroded an entire generation's faith in human progress, and eco-anxiety is taking a dreadful toll on the wellbeing of billions worldwide. The scientific community has been complicit in cultivating this corrosive mindset because far too many of us have failed to study and understand technology well enough to see how it offers the only viable path forward for our civilization. This failure is inexcusable, and the consequences have been grave. We can and must do better.

Thankfully, a *real* solution to climate change has finally come into clear view. The disruption of energy, transportation, food, and labor by clean technologies will enable us to rapidly shift away from using fossil fuels, combustion engines, and animal agriculture, while at the same time making it affordable to restore the climate system to a safe state by withdrawing hundreds of billions of tons of carbon from the atmosphere and oceans.

If all of this comes as a surprise and relief, rest assured that you are not alone. A groundswell of optimism is building, as the rise of clean technologies is making progress seem possible once again. The task now is to ensure that our individual and collective choices reflect this renewed optimism in both our personal lives and the public sphere. We must use the extraordinary opportunities granted by new technology and prosperity to become responsible stewards of our beautiful and fragile world, to repair the damage we have done in the past, and to protect it from harm in the future.

Chapter 1 Notes

[i] The degrowth orthodoxy quite rightly criticizes GDP as a flawed and misleading metric, because it is only a measure of productivity – and an imperfect one at that. The logic of using GDP as a policymaking tool is as follows: 1) production is broadly equal to consumption; 2) consumption is broadly equal to material prosperity; 3) material prosperity is a strong correlate of overall quality of life; therefore 4) GDP is a reasonable indicator of human wellbeing. But GDP does not measure everything that contributes to wellbeing. Moreover, some forms of economic productivity are actively *contrary* to wellbeing. A natural disaster that destroys thousands of homes, for example, will trigger a boom in productivity – but that should not be viewed as source of wellbeing. Many alternate metrics of wellbeing have been proposed. Nevertheless, for our purposes here, the logic of GDP as a proxy for material prosperity borne of *producing* goods and services holds. Figures for GDP per capita are typically reported either raw or adjusted for 'purchasing power parity'. The former is considered a better reflection of productivity, whereas the latter is a figure that better represents what a dollar can actually buy. $12,500 is the unadjusted figure reported by the World Bank for 2021. The figure adjusting for 'purchasing power parity' is about $18,500, which reflects the fact that the same amount of money goes a lot further in places where prices of goods are lower.

[ii] A number of schools of thought in the larger arena of sustainability incorporate the idea of restoration into their organizing principles. Examples include *regenerative agriculture* and *regenerative capitalism*. There is intense disagreement and debate about the role of technology within these different schools of thought.

CHAPTER 2

THINKING CLEARLY ABOUT THE FUTURE

"The future ain't what it used to be."

– Yogi Berra

It is crucially important that readers understand why the premise of this book is not just that technology is our best hope, but that it is our *only* hope.

In the last chapter, we began by invoking an analogy of fire. This analogy illustrates the crucial point that thinking we can solve climate change – the greatest environmental issue of our time – by slowly reducing emissions to eventually reach net zero later this century, as many prominent policy proposals have suggested for the last two decades, is no different than thinking we can save a burning building by slowly putting out the fire over days instead of within minutes and then never bothering with repairs. It is sheer delusion.

The upshot here is that we are long past the point where the planet will quickly heal itself if only we stop harming it. The enormous inertia of planetary systems means that devastating climate change impacts are *already* inevitable based on the greenhouse gases we have emitted so far, unless we actively intervene and restore the atmosphere and oceans to safe conditions.[13]

Note that a critical implication follows here:

It is physically impossible to solve climate change by reducing consumption alone.

No amount of frugal belt-tightening or environmentally conscientious lifestyle changes will pull even a single gram of carbon out of the air, just as no amount of hosing water on a burning house will repair a single brick or board.

Climate change is therefore a far, *far* greater problem than most policymakers or members of the public realize. Most are still under the false impression that our problem is merely one of overindulgence, and that if only we all bicycled to work, reused our grocery bags, and stopped eating so much meat then everything would be fine. This is dangerously wrong, and far too many of my fellow environmental scientists have either stood idly by or even helped perpetuate this myth out of fear of being branded alarmists.

If you feel shocked or angry for never having heard about this before, you have every right to be. It is absolutely disgraceful that my colleagues in the scientific community have allowed this misconception to persist for so long.

To actually solve climate change and save our world as we know it, we must withdraw the better part of two centuries' worth of carbon emissions – something on the order of 500 billion tons – from the atmosphere and oceans within the next few decades.[14,15] This is an absolutely monumental challenge, and the only possible hope we have of meeting it is with the help of advanced technology.

But make no mistake, there *is* hope! As we will see throughout the remainder of this book, the technological tools we need to meet the full challenge of climate change and other environmental crises are within reach – if we are wise enough to make the right choices today.

The environment and the future

Because of my focus on understanding technology, I am often accused of being a 'futurist' – as if that were an insult, and not a complement! But this is a puzzling irony.

Environmental issues are inherently long-term concerns. For a problem like climate change, we cannot think in terms of tomorrow's news headlines, next quarter's earnings, or next year's election cycles. Sustainability requires us to think decades ahead. The environmental sciences and humanities together with environmental policymaking, planning, and advocacy are therefore all explicitly future-oriented disciplines. On the time scale of decades, however, there is one driver of global change that now trumps all others: technological progress.

So then why aren't all environmentalists already 'futurists' like me?

Given the outsized role that technology will inevitably play in shaping our future, we cannot think seriously about the decades ahead without a clear understanding of the nature and trajectory of technological progress. Does it not stand to reason, then, that understanding technology – how and why it advances slowly or quickly, what risks and opportunities it poses, which specific capabilities it will create, and on what timeline it will render certain problems solvable – should be of paramount importance to all of the environmental disciplines? Shouldn't this be an essential component of the curriculum for our students trained in those disciplines? And shouldn't it be central to the environmental activism that those disciplines inform as well?

Yet, this is not at all what we see. Indeed, an outside observer might be forgiven for thinking the *opposite* was true: that environmental science, scholarship, policy, planning, and activism have all made a concerted effort to actively *ignore* the implications of technological progress.

What is going on?

Understandable antipathy toward technology

Since its inception in the 1960s, modern western environmentalism has had an antagonistic view toward technology, and with good reason. Over the last 150 years our growing capacity to manipulate the physical world at large scales with heavy machinery combined with our reckless use of synthetic chemicals – both of which are direct applications of fossil fuels – has taken a terrible toll on the planet's ecosystems. We have lifted humanity to previously unimaginable heights of prosperity with these potent instruments of modernity, but at great cost to the rest of nature, and only the most unapologetic technophile would refuse to concede that the tools themselves are least partly to blame for the damage we have done to the planet by using them.

There are also unequivocal associations between technology, capitalism, colonialism, and ecological destruction. The profit motive drives firms to minimize costs by externalizing them, and much if not most environmental damage is therefore caused by industries that are not held accountable for the full ecological footprint of their activities. Although this is not the fault of technology per se, powerful tools can certainly amplify the negative impacts of irresponsible behavior. And while capitalism can be a tremendous force for good, it can also be very destructive unless it is carefully regulated. Moreover, hegemonic western institutions of commerce and governance have been repeatedly foisted upon poorer nations by richer ones with grand promises of technological modernization and sustainable economic growth, but all too often the benefits of development fail to fully materialize while at the same time the richness of traditional knowledge, practices, and culture is lost.

For these reasons, antipathy toward technological advancement within the environmental movement is often conflated with animosity toward corporate greed and imperialism. Confusing correlation with causation is an understandable mistake, of course, but a mistake all the same.

Unfortunately, the resulting moral intuition of many environmentalists is not just that the societies who benefited from past greed and conquest ought to be held accountable for the damage they have done, but that they should not be allowed to innovate their way out of problems that their own irresponsibility and hubris created in the first place. Again, this is quite understandable, and justice may indeed demand some recompense in certain cases. But it would be a tragedy if our thirst for retribution prevented us from bringing every available tool to bear on the environmental crisis that we all now face.

There is no question that technology has played a role in facilitating both ecological and cultural destruction in the past, and it is of course essential that we consider any possible risks of future advancements with great care. But reflexively demonizing all new technology and dismissing its potential to solve environmental problems is neither helpful nor justified. To our discredit, this stance is all too common among we environmentalists – so much so that we have the pejorative term *techno-fix* dedicated to the task.[16] Like most pejoratives, the term is a symptom of intellectual laziness because it serves as an excuse to paint with a broad brush and avoid doing the hard work of actually evaluating matters on a case-by-case basis. This is discouraging not only for what it means looking ahead to the future, but also for reflecting on our past, because it signifies a gross under-appreciation of the ways in which technology has already allowed us to make enormous environmental progress.

For example, it might surprise some readers to learn that automobiles were originally celebrated as a solution to urban environmental problems – namely, that the streets of densely populated cities like New York and London were often covered in several *feet* of horse manure and rotting carcasses which posed a grave threat to public health and killed hundreds of thousands worldwide each year in the absence of modern sanitation systems.[17]

Figure 1: Horse manure on the streets of New York City.

Image source: unknown, circa 1894.

Similarly, before the chlorination of water supplies, waterborne diseases from natural sources of freshwater such as wells and rivers killed countless millions – mostly infants and children under five years old – and even today still cause over 2 million deaths each year.[18]

And before gas and electric stoves, the smoke from perfectly natural wood and biomass-fueled cookfires inside homes caused more disease and death than all other sources of air pollution combined – an environmental problem that in the poorest countries today still kills over 4 million people per year.[19]

It is easy for we environmentalists in the 21st Century to romanticize the ecological and sanitary conditions of the past, much like how certain political groups romanticize the social and economic conditions of the past. As the saying goes, nothing is more responsible for the good old days than a bad memory.

In a similar vein, it is all too easy to romanticize the traditional practices of indigenous cultures. There are certainly examples of such practices that are more sustainable than their modern counterparts, but it is important to recognize that traditional practices can seldom successfully scale to meet the needs of 8 billion people – if they easily could, then there would have been little incentive to develop modern alternatives in the first place. And the problem of selective memory applies here too, because traditional practices were not always benign. Burning and clear-cutting forests is not a modern invention, nor is hunting species to extinction or allowing livestock to overgraze the landscape resulting in soil erosion and desertification, to take just a few examples.

Ultimately, we do both ourselves and the environment a disservice by indulging the illusion that there is a trouble-free Edenic past to which we might return if only we could muster the will to make the necessary sacrifices.

Undue pessimism

In addition to misguided nostalgia for the past and the primitive, we environmentalists suffer from the same misapprehensions as everyone else with respect to the current state of human wellbeing worldwide. The data are clear: life is unequivocally better now in more ways for more people in more places than at any prior period in human history.[20] Figure 2 presents the data of several key indicators that show humanity has made enormous progress in becoming healthier, wealthier,

and wiser over the last two centuries – and that we have
continued to improve right up to the present day.

Figure 2: Progress in human development.

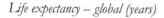
Life expectancy – global (years)

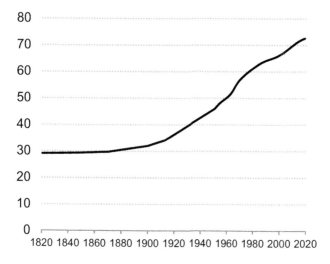

Real GDP – global ($ billions)

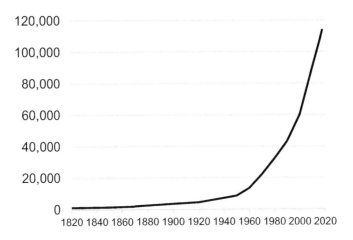

Literacy – global (% of adults)

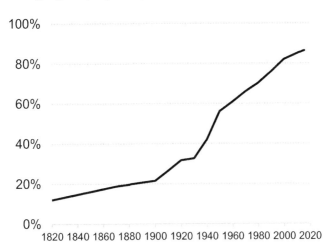

Child mortality – global (deaths per 100,000)

Extreme poverty – global (% living on less than $1.90 per day)

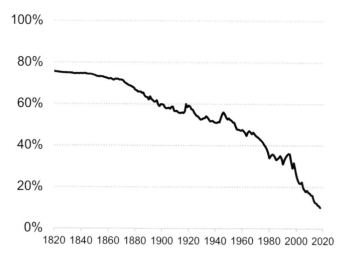

Source: Ourworldindata.org.

There are of course ups and downs along the way, and the recent COVID-19 pandemic and war in Ukraine are painful reminders that the path of progress can have treacherous twists and turns. Nevertheless, the overall trajectory is clear and inexorable. Yet, on surveys about global trends in poverty, literacy, crime, peace, democracy, civil rights, happiness, and other key dimensions of social and economic development, members of the public consistently underestimate how much progress we have made. Indeed, the majority of people are so badly misinformed about the current state of affairs that on responses to survey questions they are less correct than if they had simply guessed the answers at random. And importantly, their errors are always on the side of pessimism.[21]

The explanation for why this is the case appears to be some combination of natural cognitive biases, the news and social media's focus on negative stories, and the failure of our education system to help people cultivate a more accurate worldview. Regardless of its exact causes, there is widespread belief that life is getting worse for most people in most places, and that the world in general is headed to hell in a handbasket. This pessimism is wholly a product of ignorance and is just plain wrong.

Of course, this does not mean that the world is better in *every* way for *every* person in *every* place *all* of the time, or that there is no room for improvement. Inequality, for example, is on the rise in many countries precisely because there *has* been progress – but progress whose benefits have not been distributed fairly. (For illustration, if an entire society were destitute and then half of its people were lifted out of poverty, that is undeniably progress, but the result is, mathematically, also an increase in inequality). Nevertheless, with extremely few exceptions, the great-grandparents of almost everyone alive worldwide would have given an arm and a leg to have the quality of life that their descendants have today.

This doesn't mean the status quo is acceptable. The world is still filled with dreadful problems that we must solve as soon as possible. The fact that millions of children still die each year from easily preventable causes like diarrheal illness is totally unacceptable, even if that number is a fraction of what is used to be. The fact that millions of people still live in abject poverty alongside billionaires is totally unacceptable, even if the proportion of people in poverty has plummeted over the last century. Life isn't perfect and it isn't fair, and that means we still have a lot of work to do. But life really is *better* for more people in more places for more of the time than at any prior period in human history, and anyone who says otherwise is either ignorant of the facts or lying to push another agenda.[22]

Concerns about environmental issues, however, are different. Life is *not* better for the world's ecosystems today than it was in the past. By nearly every measure, the health of the biosphere really is in steep decline.

That said, pervasive misconceptions about social and economic progress have polluted our collective consciousness with a general pessimism that makes it difficult for us to recognize the few strides we have in fact already made toward addressing environmental issues. This in turn has made it difficult for most of us to see just how feasible the prospect of making more progress toward sustainability – indeed, *tremendously* more progress – actually is.

A legacy of doomsaying

Beyond the general pessimism that so many of us harbor, there is also a long-standing contingent among environmentalists that actually takes perverse pleasure in the fact that human prosperity has so often come at the cost of environmental degradation. The reason they do so is not because they dislike nature, but because they romanticize the relationship between humanity and the natural world as a story of perpetual struggle in which we humans are the villains.

Although aspects of this mindset can be found in cultures around the world dating to classical antiquity, it crystalized as a cultural force in western societies during the 18th Century.[23] Romanticism and Transcendentalism were literary, artistic, and intellectual movements that emerged in direct response to the dark underbelly of the Industrial Revolution: abysmal working conditions, grotesque exploitation of the poor and children and slaves as laborers, and horrendous environmental pollution – especially from the burning of coal. These were and still are perfectly legitimate things to be concerned about of course, but rather than seek practical solutions to these problems, the doomsayers have instead always reveled in the ongoing conflict they perceive between humanity and nature – and they eagerly await a day of reckoning when the environment will strike back and we finally get our comeuppance for our foolish Promethean ambitions.

We all love a good story about heroes and villains, but the temptation to frame environmental issues in these simplistic terms is another unhelpful impulse that we would do well to avoid indulging.

Environmental issues are solvable problems

Environmental issues are not an epic struggle that ought to be romanticized one way or the other. They are not an inescapable feature of the human condition whose woes we are fated to suffer forever. They are not a punishment from God for our hubris. They are not sins for which we must atone with abstinence or ritual sacrifice. And they are not an unavoidable price we must pay for the indulgences of our modern quality of life.

They are just problems. And problems are solvable – with the right tools.

Doomsaying, cynicism, and other forms of self-indulgent despair are a puerile and intellectually bankrupt response to our struggle to solve problems. They do not themselves represent any kind of solution – they are scarcely more than pouting. Moreover, once we actually do the hard work of creating a real solution to an environmental problem, the drama of our struggle to deal with it vanishes.

Take acid rain, for example. In the 1970s acid rain became a major environmental concern in the United States because the country was burning large quantities of coal with high sulfur content. Then flue-gas desulfurization technology became both affordable and legally mandated under the Clean Air Act, and acid rain disappeared from public consciousness as quickly as it had arisen.[24]

Human bodily waste provides another instructive example. Handling urine and feces was a miserable and unavoidable fact of life for millennia. Now it isn't in the majority of the world's countries thanks to modern sanitation, electricity, indoor plumbing, and water supply technologies. Solving the sanitation problem has of course contributed to other newer problems such as greenhouse gas emissions, but there was never anything romantic about defecating in a reeking bucket or open gutter, nor about the merciless toll of disease, suffering, and death that for thousands of years accompanied unsanitary water and toilet conditions – and which still continues to plague the poorest countries to an unconscionable degree today. Greenhouse gas emissions are another problem that we will solve in its turn, and our grandchildren will be no more nostalgic about the end of that struggle than we are today about the end of our great-grandparents' struggle to dispose of their poop and pee by hand without dying of cholera and typhoid in the process.

For some issues like sanitation and water quality we have already made so much progress that we have largely forgotten how serious these environmental problems once were. (It is well known, for example, that the Cuyahoga River in Ohio was so polluted that it caught on fire in 1969, but what is less well known is that that was the *thirteenth time* the river had burned since 1868, meaning conditions were not always more rosy in the distant past and have in fact improved a great deal in recent decades).[25] For other issues such as air pollution we have only just recently begun to make real progress in the past 20 years or so thanks to improvements in vehicle and power plant emissions. And for many issues – most notably climate change – we are still losing ground and have a great deal of work left ahead of us.

Environmental problems today

Why do we not solve environmental problems today? The answer is simple: cost. Repairing environmental degradation is expensive, and preventing it from occurring to begin with is not cheap either.

If it were easier to clean up our mess, or better yet to avoid making a mess in the first place, then we would of course do so. With few exceptions, the overwhelming majority of people across all of the world's cultures value environmental integrity and take no pleasure in the destruction of nature. In fact, there is substantial evidence that we humans harbor an instinctive affinity for other living things – a quality recognized for centuries by poets and philosophers, now formally termed *biophilia*.[26]

Political and cultural obstacles to solving environmental problems are entirely secondary phenomena that arise only when the cost of solutions is high enough to warrant serious social debate. The real challenge to solving environmental problems is therefore not to convince people or their elected representatives to care about the natural world – they already do, despite theatrics to the contrary – but rather to use innovation to make mitigation and restoration affordable enough to act upon without dispute.

So, how can we make saving the environment dirt cheap?

The answer is obvious: better technology.

Technology is our only hope

Technology is simply *practical knowledge*. Like all knowledge, technology has allowed us to solve some problems while at the same time it has led us to create others. But the solution to problems created by knowledge is never ignorance. The solution is always more and better knowledge.

In order to approach genuine sustainability, we need to reduce our overall environmental impact on the planet by at least 80%.[iii] New technology is the only plausible way to accomplish that. And yet, I would be a rich man if I had a nickel for every time one of my fellow environmentalists said, "technology cannot save us!"

This kind of thinking is not just wrong but backwards. Technology is the *only* thing that can save us.

To understand why, we need to review an equation.

In 1972, John Holdren and Paul Ehrlich proposed the now-famous I=PAT equation as a simple way to conceptualize humanity's impact on the environment.[27,28] The equation shows that a society's environmental *impact* (I) is a product of the number of people in its *population* (P) multiplied by each person's consumption or *affluence* (A) multiplied by the amount of damage incurred by each unit of consumption as determined by the *technology* used to produce it (T).[iv]

The I=PAT equation is not perfect, but despite its flaws it nevertheless has two crucially instructive implications. First, it shows that there are only three major levers we can pull to solve environmental problems: we can reduce our population, we can reduce our consumption, or we can improve our technology. And second, it shows that impact is the *product* rather than the *sum* of the three factors, meaning that they are inseparable and thus are all equally important. It is therefore a mistake (made discouragingly often even by knowledgeable environmentalists) to blame population *or* consumption *or* technology for the bulk of our environmental impact. To the contrary, the mathematical relationship between them means that they are all identically culpable. If we wish to reduce our total impact 80% by pulling only one of the three levers, then 80% is precisely how far we must pull it regardless of which one we choose, since their connectedness means they each have exactly the same leverage in the system.

Pulling the population lever is obviously not a viable path to sustainability, notwithstanding the misanthropic fantasies of collapse that some doomsayers enjoy contemplating. While it is very good news that population growth is slowing and many current projections suggest that we may stabilize at as few as 10 billion people, there is no conscionable way to reduce the global population by 80% from its current level.[29] Moreover, the population lever cannot offer a complete solution to environmental problems *even in principle* because it can only *reduce* impact (meaning it can only help extinguish the flames in our house-on-fire analogy). It cannot *undo* the damage from previous activity (meaning it cannot repair the damage from the blaze). The reason why is that it is logically impossible for population in the I=PAT equation to be a negative number.

Pulling the affluence lever has long been regarded as our best and only option by the overwhelming majority of environmental scientists, scholars, policymakers, planners, and activists.[v] But this strategy is doomed to fail. Despite heroic efforts by environmentalists worldwide for five decades, our track record of reducing affluence has been abysmal. It's no surprise why – the reason is right there in the word *affluence* itself: no significant portion of people will ever volunteer to be poorer. Even in the face of dire warnings of climate catastrophe from the world's most respected environmental scientists, beloved celebrities, and impassioned activists, the idea of self-imposed austerity has never gained any real traction even among those wealthy enough to afford it, let alone among the 1 billion people living in poorest countries who only aspire to the quality of life that those in wealthier countries have already enjoyed for several decades. And it certainly does not help that advocating for lifestyle changes carries a judgmental and sanctimonious air to it.

At the individual level, we can get people to buy *green* but we cannot get them to buy *less*. At the community level, we do have notable examples where groups have successfully solved tragedies of the commons with local governance, but unfortunately these are context-dependent and culture-specific and therefore do not readily scale up. And at the national level, an 80% reduction in affluence would mean a corresponding 80% reduction in production and consumption per capita (very imperfectly measured by GDP) that would have to be enforced by governments with draconian strictures.

According to the World Bank, global production and consumption per capita averaged about $12,500 in 2021, and so this figure would need to fall to $2,500 to approach a sustainable level – on par with Angola, Bolivia, and Tunisia. For the United States, whose production and consumption per capita is about $70,000, a reduction to that new global average would represent a nearly 97% decline. For comparison, the COVID-19 pandemic caused a temporary contraction in global production and consumption of just 3.5% but nevertheless wiped out the equivalent of 495 million full-time jobs.[30,31] A permanent reduction of 80% would be apocalyptic.[vi]

Decimating the global economy and destroying modern civilization as we know it would only exchange one catastrophe for another. Even worse, it *still* would not be enough to solve our most dire environmental problems like climate change because a decrease in affluence in the I=PAT equation, just as with population, can only mitigate ongoing impact (put out the fire), it cannot repair past damage (rebuild the house) on account of the fact that a negative quantity of consumption is logically impossible.

So, contrary to the widespread misconception that we cannot rely on technology to save us, technology is in fact the *only* viable lever we can pull.

The good news is that technology not only *can* improve quickly, it naturally *does* improve quickly as long as we incentivize innovation with the right combination of government support and market forces.

Better still, unlike population and affluence, the technology variable in the I=PAT equation can hold a negative value, meaning that it is possible for technologies to proactively repair past environmental damage instead of relying purely on natural recovery processes. For example, although an outright ban on the consumption of plastic grocery bags (which is itself a perfectly good idea) can only reduce *new* plastic bag pollution to zero, technology such as the Ocean Cleanup Array can proactively remove *existing* plastic waste from the seas and help restore marine ecosystem integrity.[32]

OK, so what about a combination of reducing consumption alongside technology improvement? Wouldn't that help? Surprisingly, the answer is almost certainly no.

Technological progress relies first and foremost on the prosperity borne of a thriving economy, and since reducing consumption (and thus GDP) even a few percent can lead to recession as we saw so painfully during the COVID-19 pandemic, any significant environmental benefits from pulling the affluence lever to reduce production and consumption would come at the opportunity cost of much greater gains foregone from the technology lever as a result. The logic by the numbers is clear: true sustainability requires us to maximize technological progress, and technological progress requires a thriving global economy.[vii]

Falling just short at the finish line

One more analogy to really drive the point home: picture any of a hundred videos on the Internet of foolhardy teenagers running up to the edge of a pool or stream, only to hesitate at the last moment instead of making the leap, and falling into the water as a result. Yes, it is foolish and irresponsible that we have gotten ourselves into such a predicament. But panicking and trying to stop and turn around at the precipice is exactly the wrong move.

Now it would indeed be both crazy and legitimate cause for dismay if the technologies required to deliver real solutions to environmental problems lay centuries away – and that has been the prevailing view in the environmental disciplines up to now: 'techno-fixes' are just science fiction. Under this orthodoxy, clean energy, clean transportation, and clean food will not be able to replace coal power stations, gasoline vehicles, and animal agriculture until 2050 or even 2100, and so hanging our hopes on them is seen as a distraction from the more pressing task of convincing everyone to massively downgrade their lifestyle today.

Worse still, this orthodoxy holds that if the public and policymakers were permitted to believe technological solutions are actually within reach, then that optimism might encourage complacency about environmental issues, which would make the job of selling sustainability as a noble sacrifice even harder. Although some of my colleagues disagree with me because the stakes are so high, I personally believe that *nobody* – not even with the very best of intentions – has the right to decide for anyone else whether or not it is 'safe' to be optimistic about the future.

Thankfully this pessimistic and cynical orthodoxy is dead wrong in any case. As the chapters ahead will show, viable technological solutions to many of our most pressing environmental problems *are* within reach, and optimism about the future of the environment has never been more justified.

False assumptions about environmental problems

All environmental problems are currently framed by three basic assumptions:

1. *Scarcity*: we assume that the supply of natural resources is dwindling.
2. *Degradation*: we assume that human activity will always have a net-negative impact on the environment, and in many cases natural recovery processes are so slow that the damage is effectively irreversible.
3. *Dependency*: we assume that humanity will always remain entirely reliant upon ecosystem services.

These assumptions will not hold forever. Indeed, they will not even hold for the foreseeable future because technological advancement will render each of them false over the next few decades. The bulk of this book is devoted to discussing the details of this paradigm shift as they pertain to major environmental problems, but illustrative examples are useful in summary here at the outset.

Regarding the first assumption, scarcity is ultimately a function of the availability of labor. It is true that beachfront property in Malibu is very limited, but setting these rare exceptions aside, the coming era of automation will radically increase the supply of natural resources. It is widely believed, for example, that the availability of freshwater will become a grave concern over the course of this century. In fact the opposite is true: automation together with cheap clean energy will make desalination, purification, and distribution of water much *more* affordable and accessible in the future.

Regarding the second assumption, environmental degradation is not inevitable, and in most cases it is not fundamentally irreversible either. Rather, degradation persists because prevention and cleanup are both expensive. But as clean energy, clean transportation, and labor automation continue to grow explosively, these costs will eventually decline by a factor of a hundred or more, thus rendering even the most daunting environmental problems like cleansing the oceans of plastic and removing gigatons of carbon dioxide from the atmosphere tractable. Even extinct species are not beyond recovery.

Regarding the third assumption, we currently depend upon the healthy functioning of ecosystems for our food, water, air, and much else. Indeed, this dependency is the primary reason most environmentalists give for why preserving ecological integrity is so important – and rightly so, *today*. But the logic behind this argument will erode as technological progress grants us ever-greater control over matter, energy, and information. Eventually, we will be able to conjure all basic necessities from machines with the wave of a hand, and although this power will of course present its own risks, it will also allow us to focus on valuing the natural world for other important reasons beyond its mere capacity to service our material needs. We will explore some of the fascinating ethical and philosophical implications of this fundamental transformation of the human condition in the closing chapter.

Within a few short decades, the three foundational assumptions underlying most of today's environmental problems will be turned on their heads. Instead of a world defined by scarcity, degradation, and dependency, new technologies will allow us to create a future of abundance, healing, and freedom.

Rethinking the future of the environment

We need to rethink the future of the environment through the lens of technology so that societies can make policy, planning, and investment choices that accurately reflect the dramatic advances we will achieve in the foreseeable future.

Foreseeable is a crucial caveat here, because although the pace of technological progress will be vastly greater than most of my fellow environmentalists believe is possible, it also follows that the time horizon for which we can make reasonable predictions is much shorter than is generally imagined.

With analysis based on a sound theoretical framework and strong empirical evidence, it is currently possible to make robust forecasts of technological advancement out to a horizon of about 15 years. At the time of this writing, it is not possible to make any meaningful *quantitative* forecasts beyond the late-2030s because technological change introduces too much uncertainty into the picture. Any publication or authority that purports to do so – of which there are many, especially in the environmental domain – must be treated with extreme skepticism.[33]

We can construct *qualitative* scenarios that are useful for policymaking and planning purposes based on reasonable assumptions out to a horizon of about 30 years, or around 2050 from this writing. But specific details beyond 2050 are effectively meaningless.[viii]

We can discuss environmental problems in *conceptual* terms out to about 50 years, or 2070 from this writing, in the context of established scientific principles. For example, we know that it is possible in principle to resurrect extinct species from tissue samples, and so it is reasonable to discuss the ramifications of that specific technology in conceptual terms – especially if our capacity to utilize it successfully in the future logically depends on our actions today, such as being sure to collect and safeguard the necessary tissue samples from endangered species while we still can.

Any time beyond 2070, however, is fundamentally unforeseeable. Technologically literate projections should therefore *never* extend beyond 2070. Barring a civilization-ending event such as global nuclear war or an asteroid strike, we will have made so much technological progress by then that it is absolutely impossible to make meaningful statements *of any kind* about the future beyond that point. This includes scenarios for climate change and other environmental issues for which there are many published examples that extend fruitlessly to 2100 and beyond. It is not enough merely to ignore these 'scenarios', which are undisciplined and therefore meaningless in the formal sense; we ought to actively condemn them as misleading.

It is also important to note that technological wildcards could emerge which render all predictions about the future moot significantly sooner than 2070. The most well-known and widely-discussed technology of this kind is artificial general intelligence, or AGI. Even the most bullish futurists doubt that AGI is likely to emerge before 2030, but beyond then it becomes an increasingly distinct possibility.[34]

Lastly, it is essential to recognize that some environmental problems will not be solvable with any technology short of a time machine. For example, even if we could somehow replicate destroyed ecological areas with perfect accuracy, their uniqueness and connection to history would still be lost – just like how no copy, however accurate, could replace the authentic Mona Lisa if it were destroyed. It is therefore paramount that we anticipate these truly irreversible forms of ecological damage today and prioritize their prevention.

A new kind of denialism

The first response from many of my fellow environmentalists will be to claim that the technological advances we will be discussing throughout this book are all science fiction that still lie centuries away. So, to be crystal clear, let me emphasize the following point:

Nothing in this book about the future of technology is even remotely controversial in the computer science, biotechnology, or engineering disciplines.

The technologies that will make energy, transportation, food, and labor radically cleaner and cheaper already exist. Solar power, wind power, and batteries that outcompete coal and natural gas are here. Electric cars and trucks that outcompete gasoline and diesel vehicles are here. Foods made with precision fermentation and cellular agriculture that are indistinguishable from animal products are here. Machine learning and automation are here. The clean technology disruptions that will spell the end of older, dirtier industries are already underway and are being driven by the same fundamental forces that for generations have delivered innovation, efficiency, and value when properly directed: creativity, hard work, smart government policy, and well-regulated markets.

We will of course also discuss the profound environmental implications of more radical advancements that still lie several decades ahead, since these are far too important and fascinating to ignore. But it is crucial to recognize that we can make enormous strides toward solving our most formidable environmental problems with technologies that are already in hand. We do not need to hang any hopes on cold fusion, warp drive, or other fantastical science fiction technologies to swoop in and save the day.

This is also not to say that there will be no be resistance from incumbent industries and the politicians they wield influence over. Powerful vested interests around older technologies are real, and we will be able to overcome them more quickly with the help of strong environmental advocacy and policy. And there certainly are a few genuine villains in environmental stories, like the executives and boards at major petroleum companies who actively planned and funded disinformation campaigns about climate change. Those criminals really do belong behind bars. But the idea that we will be stuck with fossil fuels, combustion engines, and animal agriculture for the rest of the 21st Century and therefore have no option but to deliberately torpedo the global economy with draconian taxes, prohibitions, and austerity measures is dead wrong – and purely a product of technological ignorance. We do not face nearly so long or desperate a struggle as most of my fellow environmentalists believe.

The question for we environmentalists to ask ourselves is: at what point does ignorance of technology on the part of the environmental disciplines become inexcusable? At what point does it become our obligation as responsible scholars, scientists, policymakers, planners, and activists to have a realistic idea of what the foreseeable future of technological progress actually entails? At what point does obliviousness to or dismissal of the preponderance of facts around technology constitute a form of denialism no different than the denialism around climate change we so rightly condemn?

We risk more than just the embarrassment of hypocrisy here. Failure to properly understand technological change has serious consequences. For example, the entire environmental science and policymaking community failed to correctly forecast the exponential growth of solar power that has occurred over the last 20 years – and simultaneously failed to pay attention to or learn from technology experts whose forecasts proved accurate. Worse still, our community has not owned up to this egregious error, or to the fact that we were successfully trolled for the better part of two decades by the fossil fuel industry via captive 'energy' agencies like the International Energy Agency and the U.S. Energy Information Administration into believing that it would be an entire century before renewables could compete on cost and capability with coal and natural gas. Worst of all, our failure to admit and correct past technology forecasting errors – especially in the context of climate change – risks confirming the conspiratorial narrative that says we have been deliberately downplaying the potential of technological solutions to environmental problems in order to terrorize the public into accepting a punitive policy agenda of greater taxation and more government control over private industry and individual consumer choices. This conspiracy theory is absurd of course, but the longer we keep *pretending* that our errors were not the result of technological ignorance, the more it will *appear* as though they were the product of deliberate dishonesty.

The future is brighter than we think

Technological progress will make many environmental problems that are intractable today solvable over the next several decades. Despite widespread dismay and no shortage of doomsaying, there has never been greater cause for environmental optimism. But in order to understand why, we must first understand the nature of technological progress itself.

Chapter 2 Notes

[iii] The figure of 80% is only an approximation because defining and measuring sustainability is a very large multi-dimensional challenge, and so it could be as low as 50% or as high as 99% depending on one's assumptions. In my own view, an approximate 80% reduction across all dimensions of ecological impact from their 2020 levels is a reasonable threshold.

[iv] Technically, I=PAT is an algebraic identity, not an equation, because unlike an equation it is true by definition for every value of its parameters.

[v] *Deep ecology* and related schools of thought attribute environmental problems to structural factors (i.e. social, cultural, political, economic, and institutional conditions) rather than technological limitations.

[vi] Today we usually measure production (and corresponding consumption) with Gross Domestic Product, or GDP. We also use GDP as a proxy for human wellbeing. Unfortunately, GDP is an imperfect metric on both counts because it only reflects financial transactions. On the first count, an exponentially growing fraction of productivity and consumption now lies outside of the formal economy. Your smartphone provides many functions such as navigation, photography, games, music, and so on, that were once monetized but are now so cheap as a result of the deflationary pressure of technological progress that they are no longer visible to markets. For example, up until the 1990s we paid for each individual frame of film we developed, and so taking photographs showed up in GDP, but this is no longer the case. Despite the fact that we produce and consume thousands of times more images than we did in 1990, the value (or 'utility') of all that production and consumption is invisible to GDP. In the future, all goods and services will progressively go the way of celluloid film photography, and if new markets are not created more quickly older ones erode, GDP could actually collapse toward zero as real production and consumption skyrocket – a consequence of shifting from our familiar economics of scarcity to an alien new economics of abundance. On the second count, there is a rich academic literature

exploring the shortcomings of GDP as a measure of human wellbeing, and a number of alternatives to GDP have been proposed.

[vii] Capitalism is often credited as the driving force of technological progress, but this is misleading because it is actually *value creation* that is key, and economic activity is simply a means to that end. After all, it is possible for capitalistic societies to experience extended economic recession or depression during which technological innovation grinds to a halt. Rather than credit capitalism in general, which is poorly defined in any case, it is more accurate to give credit to the specific institutions that together make thriving market economies possible. Individual rights and sovereignty, private property rights, trading rights (i.e. the right not just to produce and own but also sell goods and services), civil rights (that guarantee freedom from oppression and thus access to opportunities), rights of free speech and press, intellectual property rights (i.e. patents, copyrights, and trade secrets), rule of law to protect these rights, markets (and their regulation), currency, credit and debt, banking, corporations and limited liability, taxation, government funding of education and research, public agencies (and their gathering and publishing of data), secularism, and humanism. This constellation of public and private values, norms, laws, rules, and institutions (both formal and informal) is what together has allowed science, technology, and innovation to flourish. Each of the elements help a great deal, but the constellation is not synonymous with either capitalism or democracy. Moreover, each of these elements is a form of practical knowledge, and thus a technology, meaning that capitalism is as much a technological regime as a political, economic, or cultural one.

[viii] In formal terms, both the uncertainties around endogenous variables within predictive models as well as the influence of exogenous variables not included in those models become so large beyond a time horizon of 15 years or so that virtually all precision in the output of those models is meaningless. There are two key lessons to draw here. First, model complexity is almost entirely irrelevant for forecasting horizons beyond about 15 years, and so conventional forecasting models often suffer from *spurious sophistication*,

meaning that the very fact of attempting to account for additional factors in one's model actually introduces more error than accuracy to its predictions. And second, conventional forecasts themselves suffer from *spurious precision*, meaning that they make numerically precise predictions when in fact only broad general trends can be identified with reasonable confidence. Worse still, the viable forecasting horizon will only contract in the future as the pace of technological progress continues to accelerate. It is 15 years at the moment, but it is shrinking fast. In 2050, the viable time horizon for making accurate quantitative forecasts may be as short as a single year.

CHAPTER 3

UNDERSTANDING TECHNOLOGICAL PROGRESS

"Technology lets you do more and more with less and less."

– R. Buckminster Fuller

Today we depend on many technologies whose use takes a heavy toll on the natural environment. But that will not remain the case for much longer because of how fast technology is advancing. The reason why we are going to witness extraordinary progress so much sooner than most of us imagine is because the process by which technology improves is nonlinear and therefore deeply unintuitive. To build a working understanding of technological progress, we need to examine seven key concepts.

Concept 1: technological progress lets us do more with less.

Technology is *practical knowledge*, meaning knowledge that enables us to manipulate matter, energy, and information – the basic constituents of the physical world. This know-how manifests as both physical tools (hardware) and thinking tools (software) which we use to rearrange the collections of atoms, the things, the *stuff* that comprises the world around us, in useful ways.

It follows that technological progress improves the speed, scale, and precision at which we can manipulate matter, energy, and information for a given toll. *Toll* is a crucial factor here because it captures the relative value among different available choices of action. Whenever we choose to manipulate the world in a particular way, the toll of that action represents all of the other available choices we are willing to give up in the process. New technologies are therefore improvements over older ones to the extent that they enable us to do more with less: they either perform better for the same toll as an old technology, or they perform just as well while taking a lesser toll. In 1938, R. Buckminster Fuller termed this process *ephemeralization*, although the terms *dematerialization* and *decoupling* are more widely used today.

Other scholars of technology tend to use the term *cost* instead of toll here, but I find that doing so creates confusion because a technology's toll is more than just its immediate financial cost – it is *all* of the time, effort, resources, sacrifices, and foregone options both now and in the future that its utilization requires of us. As such, the term *toll* is more comprehensive because it encompasses other important ideas such as opportunity cost, net present value, and physical efficiency as well.

A primitive technology is therefore one whose utilization demands a great toll from us to achieve a given result, including any detrimental impacts on human or ecological health that we must eventually deal with down the road. An advanced technology is one that lets us achieve the same or better result with a lesser toll. And a *perfect* technology would be something genuinely miraculous, requiring only the proverbial wave of a wand or snap of the fingers to achieve the thing we wished to accomplish, without any cost or unwanted side effects at all. Some information technologies are nearly this magical already (although it is easy to take them for granted), such as audio telecommunications, audiovisual recording and playback, arithmetic computation, voice recognition, and search. Indeed, many of today's information technologies would have seemed miraculous not just to our distant ancestors but even to our own grandparents when they were children.

It is also important to recognize that most technologies today do not sit in isolation, but instead operate within large complexes, so that an improvement in one often reduces the toll of utilizing many others. Clean energy from cheap solar photovoltaic power, for example, will obviously decrease the toll of utilizing air conditioners, refrigerators, computers, mobile phones, and thousands of other devices and processes that depend upon electricity to function (much more on this in the chapters ahead).

Each individual technology's toll must be fairly evaluated relative to measures of its actual usefulness. Automobiles, for example, take a far smaller toll per passenger-mile or ton-mile traveled than horse-drawn carriages do because they are so much faster, more versatile, more efficient, and more scalable. Nevertheless, their overall impact on the environment (which is only one aspect of their toll, albeit a very important one) has been worse because we now transport thousands of times more passenger-miles and ton-miles using cars and trucks than we ever possibly could have with horses. This seemingly-paradoxical outcome of technological advancement is known as the Jevons Effect, named after William Stanley Jevons who first observed the phenomenon in trains and coal in 1865.[ix]

Finally, it is important to recognize that no technology is inherently good or bad in itself. The tools we develop merely empower us, increasing the speed and scale and precision of our control over the material world. That means things can and do go wrong with new technology. Sometimes technological innovation is put to deliberately terrible use, as in the case of nuclear weapons or land mines. Sometimes it is used recklessly, causing unintended but nevertheless dreadful side effects, as in the case of fossil fuels and DDT. And sometimes it even backfires, resulting in the exact opposite of what we originally intended, as in the case of social media driving us apart instead of bringing us together.[35] Tools give us new choices and amplify the consequences of our actions – both the benefits and harms. Indeed, that is their entire purpose.

But while technology itself is agnostic and value-neutral, it is crucial to remember that we human beings are not! True enough, we could destroy ourselves with technology, just as so many myths and fables throughout history have cautioned. Playing with fire, flying too close to the sun – these and other idioms warn us that we wield the power of the gods at our peril. Yet as we saw in the previous chapter, the facts are clear: technology has made human life better by nearly every measure. Should we really lay down Zeus's lightning bolt? For all its dangers, humanity has managed to use the power of technology overwhelmingly to the good. The data unequivocally show that we live longer, healthier, safer, fairer, freer, and more peaceful lives today than at any prior time in history. We have saved billions of lives and raised billions more out of abject poverty and misery with technology – with *practical knowledge* – ranging from electricity and medicine to institutions and laws. This miraculous achievement is not a testament to any inherent goodness of technology, but rather to the inherent decency of (most) human beings.

Concept 2: technological progress accumulates and accelerates.

Technological improvements accumulate because once practical knowledge is acquired it is not easily forgotten. Older technologies which are no longer in use are seldom lost entirely but rather are simply shelved in favor of superior new alternatives. Notwithstanding notable exceptions of technological losses from antiquity such as the formula for Roman concrete or the methods by which the great pyramids of Ancient Egypt were constructed, technological change tends overwhelmingly to march in the direction of progress – and all the more so in the modern era now that memory itself has been subject to staggering improvements via information technology.

Moreover, each new technology that we develop synergizes with and adds value to all of the other practical knowledge we have already accumulated. As a result, new technologies enhance the effectiveness of existing ones, which allows us to invent still newer technologies, which allows us to invent still newer ones, and so on in a virtuous cycle of accelerating advancement. This autocatalytic, self-compounding aspect of the process means that technology is not only always improving, but the average *rate* of overall progress itself tends to increase over time. This is not to say that every new technology will be a breakthrough with greater social, economic, or environmental ramifications than the last. Rather, it means that barring catastrophic setbacks for our entire civilization (which have indeed occurred, but are themselves becoming less frequent thanks to the growth of knowledge) each generation is likely to see more technological change than the one that preceded it.[x]

The significance of accelerating technological advancement cannot be overstated. Arthur C. Clarke famously said that any sufficiently advanced technology is indistinguishable from magic, and we will find ourselves wielding such technologies far sooner than most environmentalists would dare to imagine – indeed, within just a few decades. Again, this has already happened in the domain of bits: the Internet, smartphones, and other information technology were science fiction just 30 years ago. Much the same will be true in the domain of atoms 30 years from now.

In numerical terms, acceleration is deeply unintuitive. How many times can you fold an ordinary piece of paper in half? Most of us are surprised to learn that the answer is just seven times. The reason why is that the rate at which we are adding new layers with each fold is not constant but is accelerating. After seven doublings, the eighth would require us to fold 2^8 or 256 layers – an impossible task unless you start with a sheet of paper the size of a tennis court. This familiar example from childhood shows that acceleration is deeply unintuitive because it can produce large numbers very quickly.

The first affordable consumer digital cameras went on sale in 1994, but because the rate of adoption accelerated so dramatically after the technology became widely available, the market share of film cameras collapsed from 100% to under 1% in just over a decade.[36] Kodak, the company that had been synonymous with photography for more than a century, went from being worth $30 billion to being bankrupt in ten years. During the same time period, mobile phones went from being a clunky gimmick for the rich to a global necessity with billions of users worldwide, and today's smartphones make earlier visions of futuristic devices such as Captain Kirk's communicator look like cheap toys.[37]

The Internet itself scarcely existed in 1992: the world's first web browser was still a year away, only a handful of scientists and tech enthusiasts used email, digital music was in its infancy, and e-commerce, search, and streaming video were still science fiction. But just 15 years later the first iPhone launched in the summer of 2007, and at the time of this writing the five largest American companies are Apple, Microsoft, Amazon, Google (Alphabet), and Tesla – together worth nearly $10 trillion.

It isn't just computer technologies whose adoption grows exponentially. In automobiles, disc brakes grew from under 1% market share in 1965 to nearly 100% by the late 1970s.[38] In trains, diesel locomotives went from 5% of the market to 95% of the market between 1940 and 1955, while the coal-powered steam locomotives they disrupted did the opposite.[38] And in aviation, powered aircraft went from the Wright Brothers' first flight in 1903 to being a defining element of World War I just over a decade later. We even see evidence for rapid adoption in ancient technologies, such as neolithic arrowheads. These are just a few among hundreds of examples throughout history.

In recent years it has become fashionable to use the term *exponential growth* as a synonym for acceleration in technology discourse, and although there are some mathematical reasons to nitpick the technical accuracy of doing so, there is no need to make a great fuss over it.[xi] What matters is that the swiftness with which new technologies disrupt well-established incumbents often catches us by surprise, and the reason why is that exponential growth is profoundly unintuitive.

The perpetual challenge that exponential growth poses to our intuition is underscored by an intriguing historical irony. One of the earliest and most renowned analyses of growth, *An Essay on the Principle of Population* published by Thomas Malthus in 1798, was explicitly centered on the limits of natural resources. Malthus argued that Europe would soon be unable to grow enough crops to feed everyone because the human population was doubling so frequently. He was wrong. Although societies in Europe and elsewhere had indeed seen their populations oscillate as they ran up against food supply limits in prior centuries, Malthus incorrectly assumed that the conditions of the past would continue indefinitely into the future. He never imagined that any real improvements in agricultural productivity were possible, let alone the enormous advancements that new technology would bring. Had he published his essay 500 years earlier he would be remembered very differently, but the timing of his predictions at the dawn of the Industrial Revolution could not have been worse.

Two centuries later, in the 1970s, one of the pioneering applications of computer-assisted systems dynamics modeling followed in the spirit of Malthus with an analysis of population and natural resources that culminated in *The Limits to Growth*, which remains one of the most influential environmental books written to date.[39] Yet the reason why neither Malthus's original prognostications of collapse nor those of more recent neo-Malthusians have ever come to pass is because technology has been growing exponentially right alongside population. Ironically, my own research team uses the very same kind of systems dynamics modeling tools to analyze technology improvement and adoption that the authors used to analyze resource depletion in *The Limits to Growth*. But I do not mean to disparage my colleagues for their errors here. Rather, the point is that it is only possible to make the mistake of being deeply concerned about accelerating population expansion and resource depletion on the one hand while simultaneously remaining oblivious to accelerating technological progress on the other is because exponential growth is so darned unintuitive. If it were less alien to our instinctively linear way of thinking, the parallels would be so automatically obvious that no one could miss them.

Concept 3: technological progress follows a consistent pattern.

Even though the overall rate of technological progress is accelerating, changes within any given practical domain take place in fits and starts. Individual technologies tend to form incumbent paradigms that are stable for a time before being abruptly supplanted by a superior new alternative that forms the basis of the next paradigm in its turn. We call these rapid transformations *technology disruptions*.[40] For technologies as different as neolithic arrowheads are from automobiles, as different as carpenter's nails are from car tires, as different as smartphones are from insulin, we see the same underlying pattern of disruption occurring again and again throughout history.

We can visualize how a disruptive new technology is adopted in one of two ways, both of which are shown together in Figure 3.

Figure 3: Technology adoption curves.

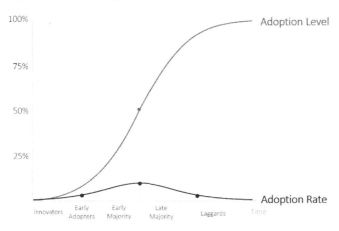

On the one hand, we can chart the cumulative *adoption level*, in which case we almost always see a *sigmoid* or *s-curve* pattern that has come to be synonymous with technology disruption. (This is also visible in Figure 7).

Alternatively, we can chart the *adoption rate* over time instead. Whether it is smartphones or any other disruptive technology, the rate of adoption naturally starts out slow, then speeds up, and then after peaking slows down once again as market share approaches saturation. This low-high-low pattern produces a *Gaussian* or *bell-shaped* curve. (Readers may recall from their calculus courses that there is a direct connection between s-curves and bell-curves: the s-curve is the *integral* because it is charting the cumulative quantity, and the bell-shaped curve is the *derivative* because it is charting the rate of change). Everett Rogers was perhaps the first researcher to fully analyze these dynamics in his landmark book *Diffusions of Innovations* in 1962, and since then technology theorists have proposed a number of explanations for why this pattern arises.[41,42]

The available empirical data show that technologies of all kinds, from ball point pens and fabric dyes to microwave ovens and flat panel televisions, have traced this same pattern of disruption.[38,43]

Figure 4: Microwave adoption s-curve (% households).

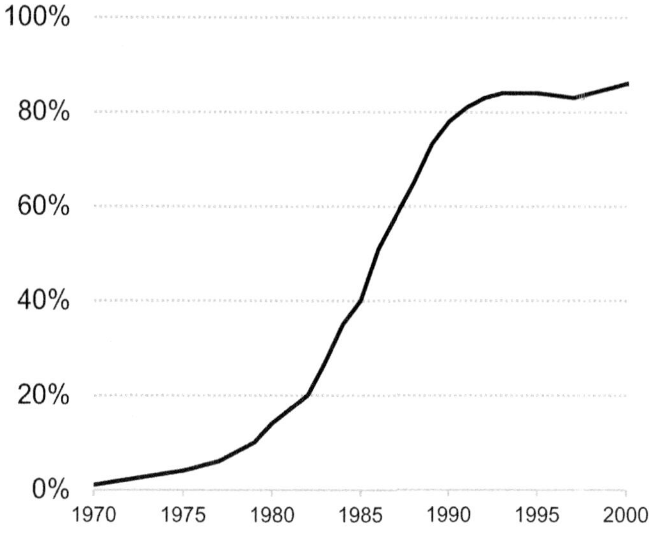

Data source: Asymco, 2018.[38]

At the same time that new technologies are being adopted, the older incumbent technologies that are being superseded decline commensurately. When presented on the same graph, the rise of the new and fall of the old form what we call a *disruption x-curve.*

Figure 5 shows the x-curve for film cameras being disrupted by digital cameras.

Figure 5: Film and digital cameras disruption x-curve (% market share).

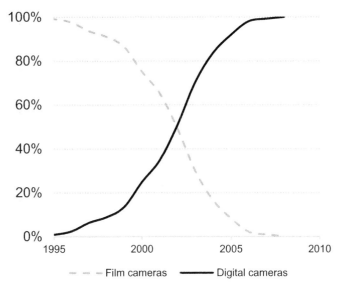

Source: CIPA, 2019; RethinkX, 2022.

Note that market *share* is not the same as market *size*. In most cases a disruptive new technology will not only capture market share but will also expand the size of the market as well – as in the case of smartphones shown in Figure 6.

Figure 6: Camera and smartphone disruption x-curve (millions sold).

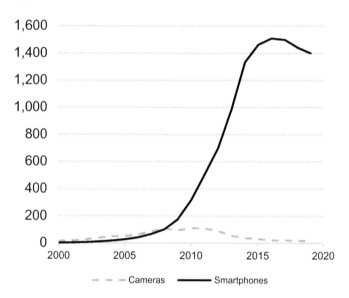

Source: CIPA, 2019; RethinkX, 2022.

Automobiles, to take another example, did not just provide a one-to-one replacement for the horse in existing applications, but because of their vastly greater speed, power, and varieties of form opened up dozens of new applications as well – for personal mobility, for hauling cargo, for farm and construction work, for combat, for recreation, for racing, and so on.

It is important to mention here that whether or not a new technology causes a disruption depends on two enabling conditions. First, in order for any new technology to continue growing exponentially as described above, it must have the potential to become significantly cheaper than the older technologies it is disrupting. Second, in order to fully disrupt existing alternatives, a new technology must be a comprehensive substitute for them, meaning that it is better in virtually every respect and not just in a few select ways. These two enabling conditions must be met in order for a new technology to cause a disruption, but the corollary of this fact is that when they *are* met a disruption is virtually inevitable.

In most domains (with the exception of computing, which we will discuss shortly), progress tends not to be continuous. Instead, long periods of only gradual improvement are punctuated by disruptions. Over time, what emerges is a trajectory of *punctuated equilibrium* – a term borrowed from ecology and evolutionary biology – as shown in Figure 7.[xii] Simple linear projections based on the recent past can provide reasonably accurate forecasts during the long quiescent periods, but they fail spectacularly when disruption is imminent (shown in Figure 7 as black arrows). This underscores the importance of being able to see disruptions coming in advance.[40]

Figure 7: Punctuated equilibrium of technological progress.

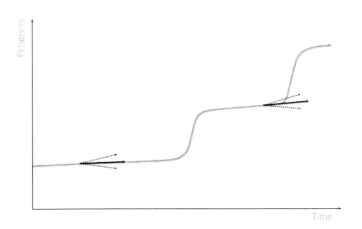

(For readers interested in additional details about the theoretical framework and corroborating historical evidence that my team uses for our technology disruption research and forecasting, resources are available online at the RethinkX website).

Concept 4: Accelerating technological progress is driven by feedback loops.

Causal feedback loops are a fundamental feature of complex systems because they stand in contrast to simple causal chains. In a causal chain, each link only affects the next link in the sequence, like falling dominoes (Figure 8).

Figure 8: A simple causal chain.

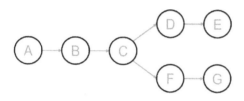

By contrast, in a complex system each element can affect any other element, creating feedback loops, as shown in Figure 9.

Figure 9: A complex system of causal feedback loops.

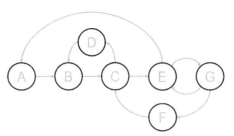

Feedback loops exist in complex systems of all kinds – from physical systems such the atmosphere, to ecosystems such as forests, to biological systems such as our metabolism, to engineered systems such as thermostats, to social systems such as markets.

The adoption of a new technology is subject to many self-reinforcing and mutually-reinforcing causal feedback loops. At the same time, the corresponding collapse of old technology is driven by feedback loops as well. New technologies therefore benefit from a virtuous cycle, while old technologies suffer from a vicious cycle (these cycles are sometimes referred to as *flywheels*). Moreover, these two cycles are connected and therefore amplify one other, as shown in Figure 10.[xiii]

Figure 10: Technology adoption feedback loops.

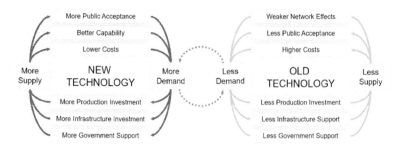

As the cost and capability of a new technology improve, market demand for products and services based on that technology grows. More market demand attracts more investment in production capacity and infrastructure to support the technology, and that investment in turn expands market supply. As supply increases, the industry gains experience and economies of scale, which loops back to lower costs and improve capabilities even further, accelerating the virtuous cycle.

As the new technology becomes cheaper and more capable, public acceptance of it grows as well, shifting from skepticism to enthusiasm – from both the public and governments alike. In the case of solar PV, for example, the public worldwide has begun to embrace rather than resist the technology now that it is affordable, and at the same time governments are using subsidies to artificially lower costs below market rates, place large orders for publicly-owned facilities, established portfolio standards for utilities that require a minimum amount of electricity to be produced from renewables, and in some areas like California have even mandated that all new homes be constructed with rooftop solar panels. All of this accelerates the virtuous cycle.[44]

At the same time that the new technology is benefiting from the virtuous cycle of accelerating adoption growth, it is stealing demand away from goods and services based on the older technologies. As a result, the older technologies experience a vicious cycle of decline where less demand means less revenue, narrower margins, less profit, and ultimately less investment in production and supporting infrastructure. For incumbent industries in the throes of being disrupted, the cost of capital rises because investors will rightly perceive mounting risk in any bets placed on the old technology, and this is only exacerbated by simultaneous decline of government support for the old in favor of the new. In September of 2019, for example, 130 banks with a combined $47 trillion in assets announced they would cease lending to fossil fuel companies and projects.[45] As the incumbent industries contract, public opinion diminishes as well. In the case of energy, the incumbent fossil fuel industries are rapidly coming to be seen as outdated, socially and environmentally irresponsible, and expensive. The erosion of both public and government support for an environmentally destructive technology equates to revoking its social license. Many governments around the world have now proposed bans on fossil-fueled cars and trucks after 2030 as part of their future policy platforms.[46]

As supply of the old technology contracts, the network effects of having a large captive user base follow suit, which serves to reduce demand even further. Incumbent industries with high operating leverage, particularly those dependent upon long-lived assets or infrastructure that requires high utilization rates, are especially vulnerable to the vicious cycle of disruption. Shrinking demand drives an upward price spiral as fixed costs must be spread over fewer and fewer units sold, and higher prices only cause demand to shrink even more. Likewise, for industries that have heavy debt loads or other obligations such as contingent liabilities, declining demand makes these obligations increasingly difficult to meet.[xiv] And finally, for industries whose finances are structured around a confident reliance upon continuous growth, the prospect of a permanent downturn in demand or commodity prices can quickly drive the entire industry into bankruptcy.

That is a lot of abstraction, so here is a concrete example: the coal industry in the United States has collapsed in the last decade, after generations of reliable growth.

Figure 11 shows the Dow Jones U.S. Coal Index, which tracks the stock market value and thus the prospects of the American coal industry from the perspective of investors. The index fell over 99% from a high of over 500 in 2011 to under 5 in 2020, and in September of 2020 the index itself was quietly discontinued. This once-giant industry has been decimated by technological disruption, first from natural gas fracking, and now by solar and wind power.

Figure 11: Collapse of the Dow Jones U.S. Coal Index.

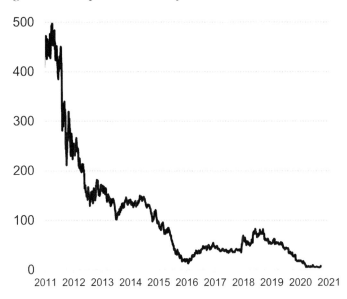

Data Source: S&P Global, 2021.

The lesson here is that even titanic incumbent industries sink very quickly when disruption strikes.

Concept 5: Computers accelerate all other technological progress.

Computers are a general-purpose technology that enables and enhances almost all other technologies. This is because all technology is practical knowledge, and improvements in information processing naturally facilitate the development and application of knowledge in general. Moreover, we are now reaching the point where the design and manufacture of advanced new technologies itself depends on computers.

Computers are already integrated with and embedded within other technologies of all kinds, from cars to coffee makers, and the clear trend looking ahead is toward what technologists call *ubiquitous computing* or *ambient intelligence,* where the human-made world is saturated with information processing capability. However, in order to realize staples of science fiction such as photorealistic virtual reality and high-resolution 3D printing, we will need truly colossal quantities of computational power.

Fortunately, to the surprise of almost everyone, the power of computers per constant dollar has done nothing but grow exponentially for over a century and shows little sign of slowing down. Since 1900, the number of calculations per second that can be purchased for an inflation-adjusted dollar has grown by a factor 10^{19} or 10,000,000,000,000,000,000. That is ten *quintillion* times. The data behind this figure must be presented on a logarithmic plot (Figure 12) whose vertical y-axis is itself exponential, otherwise the chart would be several *light years* tall – it would run off the top of the book, out your window, up into the sky, past all of the planets in our solar system, and well beyond the nearest stars. The astronomical advancement of computer technology is the reason why a device that costs a few hundred dollars and fits in your pocket today is hundreds of thousands of times more powerful than the million-dollar supercomputers that took up entire floors at NASA half a century ago.

Figure 12: Exponential growth of computing (performance per

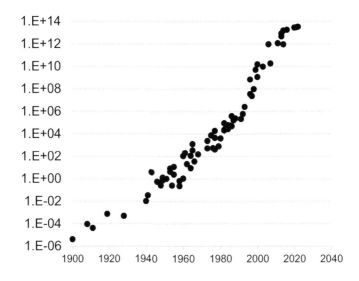

dollar).

Source: RethinkX, 2022.

One key feature to notice about Figure 12 is that the growth in computing power has been extraordinarily consistent. Wars, revolutions, and recessions have had almost no discernible impact on the trend. *Moore's Law*, the famous observation by Intel cofounder Gordon Moore that transistor density on integrated circuits doubles roughly every two years, is closely associated with the exponential growth of computer power, but the exponential growth of computing actually predates integrated circuits by more than 60 years. This pattern has persisted across five major paradigm shifts in hardware and architecture: the first computers were mechanical tabulators made of levers, cogs, and gears. These were supplanted by machines with electromechanical relays, then vacuum tubes, then simple semi-conductor transistors, and finally today's integrated circuits.

How long this can continue is uncertain. It is difficult to predict exactly when the self-reinforcing feedback loops driving this exponential progress will begin to give way to self-limiting ones, and thus where the exponential curve will finally inflect into an s-shaped curve. Moore's Law, which only applies to transistor density, will come firmly to an end in the 2020s as we reach the physical limits of 2D integrated circuits in silicon. But computing power itself may nevertheless continue to become exponentially cheaper, and new hardware paradigms such as 3D circuits and quantum computing paired together with new software such as deep neural networks and differentiable programming – among many others – offer a number of possible avenues for continued advancement.

The ultimate limits of computation allowed by the laws of physics lie far beyond what we have accomplished to date. At present we can achieve roughly 1 quadrillion or 10^{15} calculations per second with one kilogram of hardware. This is simply astonishing by any reasonable measure. But MIT physicist Seth Lloyd has calculated that the ultimate physical limit is about 10^{40} calculations per second per kilogram of ordinary matter, with a hard limit of 5.4258×10^{50} calculations per second in more exotic structures like artificial black holes, so there is still considerable room to grow.[47]

The price-performance of computer technology is improving by a factor of 1,000 roughly every 15 years, so if exponential growth continues on that same trajectory for several more decades – an admittedly big *if* – then the devices of 2050 will be a million times more powerful than those of

2020 for the same price. Or, alternatively, we could have devices as powerful as our smartphones today that are a minuscule fraction of the cost and size.

Concept 6: Technology can still improve a great deal because complicated machines can be *extremely* small.

The notion that in 2050 tiny machines capable of performing trillions of calculations per second and running sophisticated software might be had by the fistful for pennies would seem to defy belief, just as the capabilities of our smartphones today would have defied belief in 1990. But this is the unintuitive power of exponential growth coupled with the fact that atoms are so very, very, *very* small.

For instance, there are more atoms in a single penny than there are grains of sand in all the beaches and deserts of the *entire world* – about 30 sextillion.[xv]

Atoms are just mind-bogglingly tiny, and the crucial implication of this fact is that extremely small machines can therefore be tremendously complicated. Just imagine how intricate a sandcastle could be if it were built using all of the sand in the world – that is how complicated a device the size of a penny could be if it were constructed atom-by-atom.

Can machines actually be constructed using building blocks at the atomic scale? Of course they can! We are surrounded by countless examples all day every day. *We* are precisely such machines! Biology is protein-based nanotechnology that builds biological machines ranging in size from microscopic to as large as giant sequoias and blue whales, all molecule-by-molecule. Even the smallest organisms are formidably complicated machines, as Figure 13 below shows.

Figure 13: Marvelous machinery – the foot of a mosquito.

Photo credit: Steve Gschmeissner, 2016.

Biology is the existence proof that technology can modify the physical world at great speed, at enormous scale, and with astonishing precision simultaneously. However, there is no reason to think that the protein-based nanotechnology we call biology is the most optimal of all possible nanotechnologies. It is certainly conceivable, and perhaps very likely, that nanotechnologies based on other substrates than protein will prove more useful for specific applications, just as exotic alloys are better than muscle and bone for building machines that fly hundreds of miles per hour, and microwave towers are better than vocal cords for transmitting gigabits of information.

The machines we build today are clunky and expensive compared to the marvels built by biology. But after just a few more decades on our current trajectory of exponential growth, technology will advance to the point that we will be able to construct machines that are comparable in size and functional capability to biological organisms. This is not to say that we will be building robots that are fully as complicated as birds, or insects, or even microbes any time soon – but that would be unnecessary anyway, because the overwhelmingly majority of biological complexity is dedicated to an organism's own internal operation: metabolism, immune response, healing, growth, reproduction, and so forth. Human-designed robots will not need to perform any of these functions. Indeed, it would be prudent to outlaw the creation of synthetic self-repairing and self-replicating machines, given the risks that such devices could pose if they were ever to escape our control. But biology provides conclusive proof that machines capable of quite sophisticated behaviors can be very small, very numerous, and very cheap. As we will see in the chapters ahead, the opportunities that large numbers of inexpensive insect-sized and microbe-sized robots present for solving environmental problems are extraordinary.

Concept 7: Scarcity is ultimately caused by a shortage of labor.

Introductory economics courses explain that *factors of production* are the inputs into any process that produces finished goods and services as outputs. Different schools of economics vary slightly in how they categorize these factors, but the list generally includes four types of inputs: 1) natural resources in the form of land, raw materials, and energy; 2) capital in the form of equipment and facilities; 3) labor; and 4) the knowledge with which to organize and combine the other three.

It follows that the economic cost of goods and services depends on the availability of these inputs. Indeed, history shows that goods and services became vastly cheaper when fossil fuels made energy abundant, when industrialization made capital in the form of equipment and facilities abundant, and when public education made both skilled labor and knowledge abundant. History also shows that as technology improves, capital (machinery) takes over and performs more and more tasks that could previously only be performed by humans. As a result, technological advances around labor have allowed many societies today to achieve a level of productivity and prosperity that from our ancestors' perspective would have defied imagination.

A key point to emphasize here is that energy and raw materials are not themselves scarce in any fundamental sense. The Earth receives more energy from the sun in an hour than our entire civilization consumes in a year, and within the planet's crust and oceans there are trillions of tons of almost every element we need. Energy is only expensive because someone has to build the solar panels and batteries to capture it, and the raw materials with which to do so are only expensive because someone has to mine and refine them, and mines and refineries with which to do so are only expensive because someone has to build and operate them, and so on.

It is therefore labor which is ultimately the limiting factor of production. As Adam Smith wrote more than two centuries ago, "The real price of everything … is the toil and trouble of acquiring it." It follows that if we had an unlimited supply of dirt-cheap labor, almost everything *else* would be dirt cheap too.

Note that there is a crucial difference between *labor* and *work*. A bulldozer can do more *work* in an hour than a hundred humans with shovels can do in a month, but the bulldozer is *capital* whereas the people who operate it – or design it or build it or repair it – are the ones doing the *labor*. Work can be mindless and purely mechanical, but labor requires *intelligence* – or at the very least many aspects of it, such as observing, recognizing, modeling, planning, navigating, and decision-making. In other words, work can be *mechanized* but labor must be *automated*.

Human labor will be disrupted by *machine labor* over the next two decades, and the pebble that triggers the automation avalanche will be autonomous vehicles. After all, it is not hard to imagine how software that can safely navigate rush hour traffic in Los Angeles could also be adapted to shelve items and pack boxes in a warehouse, mop floors and wash dishes in a kitchen, hang shirts on a retail rack or fold them at a laundry, assemble widgets on a production line, or any of a thousand other examples. One company that clearly understands this already is Tesla, which revealed plans to develop a humanoid robot in 2021. Conventional analysts and auto industry experts were so baffled by Tesla's announcement that some thought it might even be a joke. (Nearly a decade earlier I wrote that the first company to automate driving would be positioned to lead the automation of *all* human labor. And at the time, I suspected it was the underlying reason why Google – in another example of a company venturing into seemingly unrelated territory – had entered the race to self-driving car technology in the first place).

Just to be clear, we are not talking about conscious or self-aware 'robots' like C-3PO or Commander Data that possess *general* intelligence. We are talking about machines with only *narrow* artificial intelligence of the mindless, algorithmic kind. But narrow AI alone will be enough to transform the global economy and civilization as we know it because clever algorithms go a long way, as the example of autonomous vehicles itself clearly shows.

Automation will be an environmental game-changer for two key reasons. First, it will make almost all goods and services radically cheaper – and quickly too, over the course of just one or two decades. And second, machines will be capable of doing work at a scale, speed, and precision that is either economically impractical or outright physically impossible for humans to achieve.[xvi] It is largely for these two reasons that environmental problems which today are prohibitively expensive to address will become solvable in the near future.

Why do we not pick up all litter before it reaches our rivers and seas? Why do we not recycle all waste instead of sending it to landfills? Why do we not pull weeds manually rather than blanketing entire fields with herbicide? The answer is because the labor necessary to do so is simply too expensive – *today*. But it is not difficult to imagine that software capable of driving a truck through Manhattan could be readily adapted to control a robot that picks up litter, sorts through waste, or pulls weeds. These examples give just a small preview of the extraordinary opportunities for technology-driven environmental mitigation and restoration that we will discuss in the chapters ahead.

The importance of understanding technological progress

The environmental sciences and humanities together with environmental policymaking and planning are all explicitly future-oriented disciplines because sustainability requires us to think decades ahead. But thinking seriously about the future on a timeframe of decades also demands a good understanding of technological progress and disruption.

It is therefore logically incontrovertible that all of the environmental disciplines must have technological literacy at the center of their expertise, as well as at the core of their training curriculum. To date, however, we see not only the absence of any such content, but a genuinely willful ignorance with respect to technology. This embarrassing state of affairs is nothing short of disgraceful, and needs to change as soon as possible if the environmental disciplines are to retain their relevance and legitimacy in the eyes of the public, policymakers, and other scholars and scientists going forward.

Chapter 3 Notes

ix The Jevons Effect is real, but is commonly misinterpreted to mean that new technologies are always worse for the environment than older ones, even if they are more efficient. In reality, the Jevons Effect arises from the combination of population, consumption, and technology – just as the I=PAT equation describes. For example, if the world's 8 billion people were to consume as many passenger-miles and ton-miles with horses as we now do with cars and trucks, the entire surface of the planet would look like the streets of New York in 1890: a noxious hellscape of knee-deep manure and rotting carcasses. The Jevons Effect only appears to be a paradox when we fail to recognize the interdependence of all three variables in the I=PAT equation and measure the actual value or *utility* being provided. One easy way to see through the paradox is to consider cases where new technology has indeed reduced demand for resources. For example, digital cameras (and now smartphones) did not create a Jevons Effect for celluloid film, despite triggering a million-fold increase in photograph production and consumption. This is because the value and utility of photography was not inextricably coupled to celluloid film, just as passenger-miles were not inextricably coupled to horses. The Jevons Effect is itself a specific environmental example of a more general economic phenomenon known as a *rebound effect* which results from a disproportionately large increase in consumption associated with a decrease in price resulting from high price elasticity of demand. The concept of price elasticity of demand was discovered by Alfred Marshall in 1890, and thus did not yet exist in 1865 when William Stanley Jevons first noticed the effect in energy technologies. One explanation for why energy has a high price elasticity of demand is that lower energy prices not only increase demand relative to its existing baseline but also stimulate a broad increase in economic activity that raises the baseline level of energy demand itself as well.

x Some observers argue that technological innovation has slowed down since the end of the Cold War, but these critics tend to view innovation through a 'whiz-bang' lens rather than with consistent metrics. The whiz-bang lens privileges qualitative leaps over quantifiable increments. Going from traveling by train to traveling by airplane is a huge qualitative leap because flying is inherently different than rolling. But according to the underlying metric of the cost of moving kilograms or passengers from A to B in a given amount of time, jet aircraft did not provide a great leap forward but rather an incremental improvement in travel utility available per dollar. Indeed, the reason why trains were not disrupted (i.e. eliminated as an industry) by aircraft is precisely because aircraft did *not* offer a vastly greater amount of travel utility per dollar when they were first introduced. Contrast this to digital cameras, for example, which *disrupted* film cameras precisely because they *did* offer so much more utility per dollar.

[xi] Folding paper, for example, produces *geometric* growth in the number of layers, not exponential growth. Although both are forms of accelerating change, geometric growth takes place at discrete intervals whereas exponential growth is continuous. This is because some processes like folding paper cannot be divided into arbitrarily small steps – you cannot make a partial fold or add a fraction of a layer to the stack.

[xii] The analogy here between technology and biology is not perfect. Unlike technological innovation, biological evolution is not a conscious process of design that aims to make progress toward a specific goal.

[xiii] Readers familiar with systems theory may recognize that this simplified diagram does not show stocks and flows as a standard causal loop diagram or full systems dynamics model would. Rather than connect stocks with directionally coded flows, I have found from my experience teaching university students that omitting stocks entirely and instead using only unidirectional flows (*more of* X causes *more of* Y) in the fashion of an informal flowchart makes the idea of causal feedback more intuitive and accessible to those encountering the concept for the first time.

xiv In the case of the fossil fuel industry, a key contingent liability that may enter into some of the major firms' financial statements are the costs of lawsuits and fines that they could face as a result of their previous climate change disinformation campaigns.

xv This calculation assumes a U.S. penny of pure copper minted prior to 1983 weighing 3.1 grams.

xvi Hollywood movies have created the false impression that the physical capabilities of robots will only slightly exceed those of humans. In reality, machines can exert tens of thousands of times more force than the human body and can move too fast to see. A simple Internet search for "high speed robot" videos provides dozens of eye-popping examples.

CHAPTER 4

SOLVING CLIMATE CHANGE

"Opportunities multiply as they are seized."

– Sun Tzu

C limate change is the greatest environmental problem of our time. Unfortunately, it's also a much, *much* bigger problem than most of us realize.

The good news, however, is that we already have the technological tools we need to solve climate change. Better yet, we can get the job done much faster than is widely believed. And best of all, we can do so *without* torpedoing the global economy, giving up a modern standard of living, or condemning billions to remain in poverty.

Today, over 90% of all greenhouse gas emissions come from just three economic sectors: energy, transportation, and food.[48]

Figure 14: Global greenhouse gas emissions by sector.

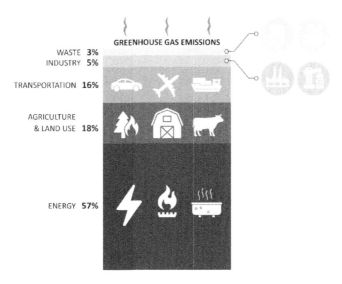

Source: Our World in Data, 2020.[48]

My team's research has shown that clean technology disruptions are already underway in each of these sectors, which will enable us reach net zero emissions worldwide before 2040. These three disruptions will be driven by just eight clean technologies, all of which are already commercially deployed today, meaning that they are science fact, not science fiction.[2]

In energy, the technologies are solar photovoltaics, wind power, and batteries, and these will disrupt coal, oil, and natural gas.

In transportation, the technologies are electric vehicles, autonomous driving, and ride hailing, which will disrupt internal combustion engines and private vehicle ownership.

In food, the technologies are precision fermentation and cellular agriculture, which will disrupt meat, milk, and other livestock and seafood products.[49–51]

Like others throughout history, these three disruptions are inevitable for the simple reason that the new technologies overwhelmingly outperform and will therefore economically outcompete the older ones. We have reached the tipping point in each sector, which means we now have the immense power of market forces working *for* the environment instead of against it. When disruption strikes, switching to the new technologies is a no-brainer because it means saving money. It also means that we no longer need to waste time and resources on an all-of-the-above scattershot approach to solving climate change, and we can dispense with unnecessary and foolhardy band-aid treatments like 'clean coal' power plants, corn ethanol for vehicle fuel, and fitting cows with fitness trackers.[52,53] Instead, we can now maximize the bang for our buck by focusing our efforts on deploying these clean technologies to eliminate the overwhelming majority of global emissions at their source.

Climate change is a much, *much* bigger problem than is widely believed

If climate change were a burning building, then greenhouse gas emissions would be the flames. To deal with this crisis, we must both put out the fire to stop doing more harm *and* we must repair the damage that has already been done.

The house-on-fire analogy helps illustrate three crucial but inconvenient truths that are not part of the conventional climate change discussion.

Inconvenient Truth #1: Even if all anthropogenic greenhouse gas emissions stopped tomorrow, many of the worst impacts of climate change would still occur.

Although there is debate among scientists about the details, it is incontrovertible to say that a number of planetary changes such as the breakup of ice sheets and the melting of permafrost represent tipping points that, once transgressed, may take centuries to naturally recover without human assistance. As if that weren't concerning enough, it is looking increasingly likely that the 1.1 °C of warming humanity has *already* caused over the last few centuries has set us on a collision course with these tipping points.

This leads directly to the next point.

Inconvenient Truth #2: It is not enough just to stop emitting greenhouse gases.

The overwhelming majority of the public and policymakers falsely believe that the atmosphere and oceans will rapidly heal themselves if only we stop assaulting them. In environmental jargon, we use the term *mitigation* to mean "stop doing harm". Following our house-on-fire analogy, the majority of people – including most well-informed and well-intentioned environmentalists – believe that we can solve climate change if only we manage to extinguish the flames by bringing net emissions to zero. This is false, and my fellow scientists know it. Mitigation alone is not enough. If we are to prevent climate catastrophe, we also have a huge amount of *restoration* to do, which means actively repairing the damage. And *soon*. Not slowly over centuries, but within the next few decades.

The scale of the climate restoration challenge ahead of us is enormous. Although the exact amount is subject to debate, we may well need to withdraw as much as 500 billion tons of carbon from the atmosphere and oceans in order to undo the harm we have done over the last several centuries and safely restore these planetary systems to a condition approximating their pre-industrial state.

This brings us to the third crucial point to address, which we already encountered at the beginning of Chapter 2.

Inconvenient Truth #3: It is physically impossible to solve climate change by reducing consumption alone.

We have long passed the point where we can avert catastrophe merely by downgrading our individual lifestyles or imposing stricter rules on corporate and state polluters. No amount of bicycling to work or regulatory standards will pull a single gram of carbon *out* of the atmosphere, just as no amount of firefighting will *repair* a damaged house. Nevertheless, the overwhelming majority of people worldwide – including most environmentalists – falsely believe that we only need to douse the flames and the house will somehow magically fix itself.

Ignorance and desperation

The three inconvenient truths above represent a long-standing and very dangerous misconception that my colleagues throughout the scientific community have allowed to persist. I have been vocally critical for over a decade about the failure of the scientific community to speak frankly about the true magnitude of our crisis, including in my own peer-reviewed publications.[54]

I cannot pretend to know the minds of my fellow scientists. I do know from personal conversations that they have been well aware of the need for climate restoration all along, but I don't know why they have been so reluctant to speak out about it. My guess – and it is only a guess – is that they have been unable to imagine (or at least propose without ridicule) any plausible way to withdraw 500 gigatons of carbon out of the atmosphere and oceans in time to actually solve climate change, and so they have avoided the topic and focused on the more manageable challenge of mitigation and reducing emissions to zero instead. I also strongly suspect this is why optimism has been so scarce in the climate science community up to now.

What can be said with certainty, however, is that those who advocate for a reduction in economic activity to solve climate change (i.e. 'degrowth' of production and consumption) are like medieval doctors prescribing bloodletting out of ignorance and desperation: 1) it won't solve the problem, 2) it will make actually solving the problem harder, and 3) it will create entirely new problems in the meantime.

First, the bloodletting treatment of reducing economic activity won't work, as we've seen from the house-on-fire analogy, because no amount of mitigating ongoing emissions does anything whatsoever to repair the damage we've already done to the atmosphere and oceans.

Second, it will make the problem worse because reducing economic activity by the amounts that advocates imagine (50% or more) on the timeframe they imagine (a decade or two) would devastate the global economy, thus undermining the very thing we need most to tackle this immense challenge: *prosperity*. The trillions of dollars, technological innovation, political will, and civil stability required to repair the atmosphere and oceans will all be much harder if not downright impossible to muster under austerity rather than amidst abundance.

Third, it will create new problems because devastating the global economy would cause a worldwide social catastrophe comparable to the climate crisis itself. Moreover, even if governments were indeed foolish enough to forcibly torpedo the global economy in the name of environmental sustainability, the environment itself would be – as it always has been – among the first casualties of the chaos, conflict, and privation that followed.

Rethinking future emissions

In 2014, the Intergovernmental Panel on Climate Change (IPCC) published its Fifth Assessment Report, which reflects the authoritative consensus among the world's environmental and climate scientists. I was still a PhD student at UCLA at the time, but I was so concerned by what I saw in the IPCC report that I immediately wrote a paper to address what I felt were fundamental misconceptions about the nature of the climate change problem and its potential solutions.

Specifically, I was shocked to see that none of the IPCC scenarios projected emissions going significantly *below* net zero until well into the second half of the century, and that most of the scenarios never went below net zero at all. That means the IPCC was ignoring the need for carbon withdrawal almost entirely.[xvii]

Figure 15: IPCC Fifth Assessment Report emissions scenarios.

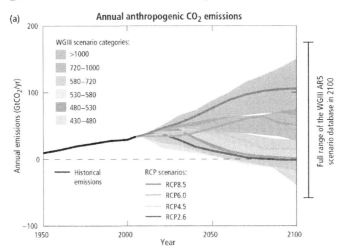

Image Source: Reproduced from IPCC, 2014.[55] (A color version is available online).

After almost two years of submissions, my paper was finally accepted in the peer-reviewed journal *Anthropocene* and published in 2016. In that paper, I presented what was then a scandalously unorthodox view of what a real solution to climate change must look like, because carbon withdrawal is a form of *geoengineering*, which at the time was a taboo subject.

My analysis showed that we must rapidly achieve not just net zero emissions but also dive deep into an aggressive carbon withdrawal regime. Accordingly, my analysis distinguishes mitigation and restoration as two distinct stages of solving climate change.

Figure 16: The anthropogenic CO_2 emissions impact pulse.

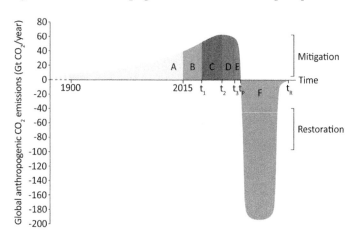

Source: adapted from Dorr, 2016.[54] (A color version is available online).

I am pleased to report that in the years since then, the IPCC has slowly begun to admit the need for carbon withdrawal. But it has not yet shifted its scenarios nearly enough to ensure a complete solution. Instead, the climate science community has largely given up on the idea of returning our climate to anything close to a pre-industrial state, and instead is focusing on limiting warming to 2 °C. But this is extremely risky, because even the 1.1 °C of warming we have *already* caused will very likely to lead to catastrophic impacts.

Ice sheets in Antarctica and Greenland are *already* melting at alarming rates. The northern polar ocean is *already* nearly ice-free in the summer. Permafrost is *already* melting and releasing methane in the Siberian and Canadian tundra. Extreme weather events like storms, floods, and droughts have *already* become more destructive and more common. And in the oceans, the increase in temperature and acidity is *already* bleaching corals and harming marine ecosystems.[56] None of these impacts are acceptable in any truly complete solution to climate change.

In short, the IPCC scenarios suggest that the climate science community believes it is already too late to really *solve* climate change, and that the best we can hope for at this point is damage control.

Thankfully, this defeatist view is dead wrong, and is purely the result of technological ignorance. We *can* solve climate change. *Fully*. And the technologies that will disrupt energy, transportation, food, and labor are the key to understanding how.

The energy disruption

At the time of this writing, the energy sector itself accounts for 57% of greenhouse gas emissions worldwide.[48] This number includes burning coal, petroleum, and natural gas for electricity generation, as well for residential, commercial, and industrial heating, but it excludes fossil fuels used in transportation. The use of energy is fundamental to meeting all of our other needs, and so fossil fuels have cast a long shadow of environmental impact across the global economy because they have been the dominant sources of humanity's energy for over a century. But this is about to change.

The disruption of the energy sector will be driven by the economics of solar photovoltaics, onshore wind power, and batteries. The costs and capabilities of each of these technologies have been improving relentlessly for several decades. Since 2010 alone, solar PV capacity costs have fallen over 85%, onshore wind capacity costs have fallen more than 45%, and lithium-ion battery capacity costs have fallen almost

90%. These cost improvements are consistent and predictable, and will continue throughout the 2020s as the technologies continue to scale.[51] Meanwhile, at the same time that costs are falling, the rate of adoption is accelerating.

The energy disruption is already underway, and all available evidence points to solar, wind, and batteries unfolding as a textbook case of technology disruption in energy.

Figure 17: The disruption of energy.

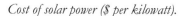

Cost of solar power ($ per kilowatt).

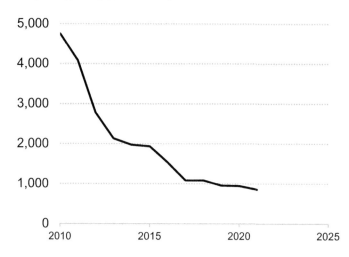

Source: RethinkX, 2022.[xviii]

Adoption of solar power (global gigawatt-hours generated).

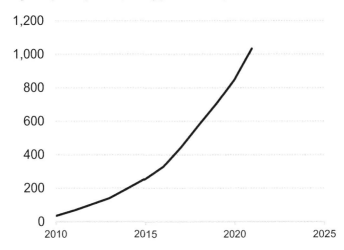

Source: RethinkX, 2022.

Cost of wind power ($ per kilowatt).

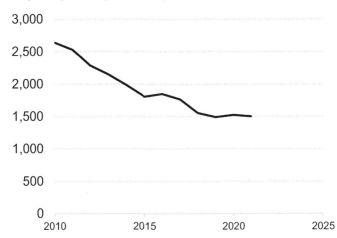

Source: RethinkX, 2022.[xix]

Adoption of wind power (global gigawatt-hours generated).

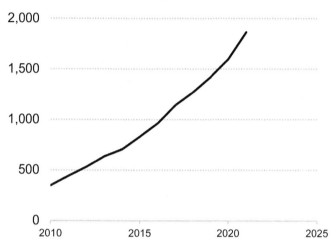

Source: RethinkX, 2022.

Cost of lithium-ion batteries ($ per kilowatt).

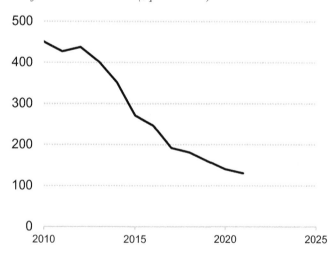

Source: RethinkX, 2022.[xx]

Adoption of lithium-ion battery storage capacity (gigawatt-hours).

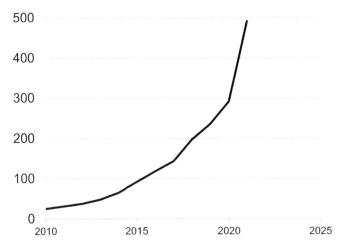

Source: RethinkX, 2022.

Another aspect in which the energy disruption is shaping up to be a textbook case can be seen in the denialism from the incumbent energy industries and agencies whose identities and expertise are centered on fossil fuels. This is a recurring pattern we see throughout the history of disruption: the incumbent telecoms industry dismissed the smartphone; the incumbent photography and film industry dismissed digital cameras; the incumbent media and publishing industry dismissed the Internet; the incumbent horse and buggy industry dismissed the automobile; and so on. This time is no different. Every year, the energy incumbents have claimed that the cost improvements and market growth of solar, wind, and batteries cannot continue, that the new technologies are no threat, and that fossil fuels still have a bountiful future. And every year, the evidence from reality flies in the face of this foolish wishful thinking.

Figure 18: Denialism from the incumbent energy sector.

IEA projections for solar power (gigawatts).

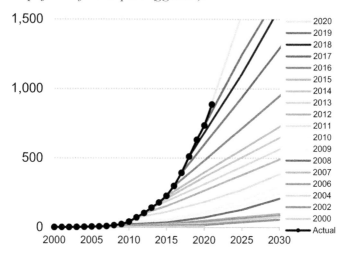

U.S. EIA projections for coal power (quadrillion BTUs).

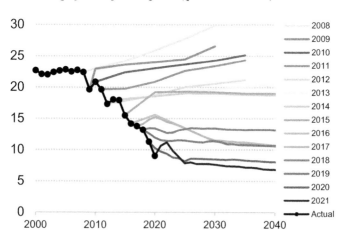

Source: RethinkX, 2021, based on U.S. EIA data. (Color versions are available online).

Unfortunately, these mistakes have grave consequences because the climate science community has chosen to trust the incumbent energy industry's forecasts over those of technology disruption experts. In the same 2014 IPCC report I mentioned before, the 'best case' scenario (i.e. the scenario with the lowest cumulative emissions and thus the smallest global temperature increase) assumed that less than 5% of the world's primary energy would come from solar, wind, and geothermal power combined by the year 2100.

Figure 19: RCP scenarios for 2100 (global primary energy use).

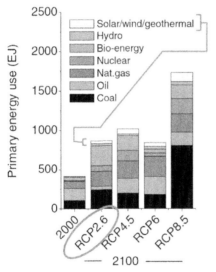

Source: Reproduced from Van Vuuren et al., 2011, and IPCC, 2014.[57–59] (A color version is available online).

However, the data showing the consistent exponential growth of solar and wind were already unmistakable by 2014, and the further data that have come in since then have only extended the trend (shown in Figure 20).

Figure 20: Solar and wind power (global terawatt-hours)

Reality vs. IPCC scenario RCP2.6.

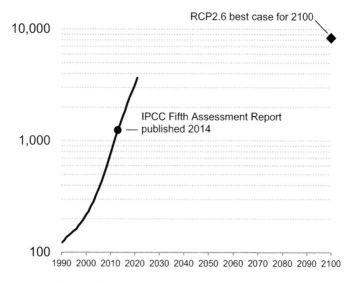

Source: RethinkX, 2021.[2]

By 2030, solar and wind power will exceed the IPCC's 'best case' scenario for the year 2100 – 70 years ahead of schedule.

The magnitude of this error is completely unacceptable with trillions of dollars and the policymaking of our entire civilization on the line, but to date the climate science community has never admitted this mistake, let alone apologized or taken responsibility for it.

The latest round of IPCC climate scenarios continue to display the same fundamental misunderstandings and errors around technology.[60] The latest 'high-technology' scenario, for example, is titled "Fossil-Fueled Development" which is not just wrong but backwards: the *highest* technology pathway will obviously involve the *most* clean energy and therefore the *least* fossil fuels.[61]

The public and policymakers should not accept this state of affairs, and should demand answers and accountability for why such egregious blunders continue to be made.

The reality of the energy disruption is simple: the old technologies cannot compete economically with the new ones. This is why over 70% of all new electricity generating capacity deployed worldwide in 2020 was solar and wind power, and why that fraction is increasing every year.[62] It is why solar and wind power leapt from providing just 3.5% of all electricity in the United States in 2012 to 25% of all electricity a decade later.[63,64] Solar and wind are of course intermittent sources of energy, which means they must be paired with energy storage in order to provide reliable electricity, but my team's research has shown that by 2030 the older energy technologies will be unable to compete with solar and wind paired with batteries that makes electricity available all day, all night, all year round.[xxi] Other research teams around the world have begun to publish similar findings.[65] As we have seen throughout history, the overwhelming economic competitiveness of the new technologies is the reason why disruptions proceed so swiftly and why their outcome is inevitable.

The energy disruption has an additional extraordinary feature: as solar, wind, and batteries adoption accelerates, these technologies will produce an increasingly large surplus of energy at near-zero marginal cost. We call this surplus of electricity *Clean Energy Super Power* (or just *super power* for short).

Because any solar, wind, and batteries system must fully meet electricity demand during the most challenging times of year such as the cloudy weeks of winter when the days are shortest, it is therefore able to produce a surplus of electricity throughout the rest of the year. When optimized correctly, the total amount of electricity produced by an such a system can be double or even triple that of a conventional grid powered by fossil and nuclear fuels, while still being much cheaper overall. The upshot of super power is that energy will become not only clean, but cheap and superabundant as well. Just as we saw enormous new opportunities and value emerge when the Internet slashed the marginal cost of information and communication to near-zero, the superabundance of clean energy will also open the door to extraordinary new possibilities for society and the economy – and of course for the environment and climate change as well. [xxii]

As energy changes from being dirty and expensive to clean and cheap, we will need to fundamentally rethink our relationship with it. In the past, the high marginal cost, environmental impact, and safety risk of fossil fuels and nuclear power strongly incentivized societies to *minimize* energy use. For several generations, we have been taught to 'conserve energy', to voluntarily minimize our energy utilization, despite the fact that energy utilization is a fundamental enabler of human prosperity and strongly correlated with human wellbeing across the board. This conventional thinking no longer makes sense for an energy system based on solar, wind, and batteries. We must instead *maximize* our utilization of solar, wind, and battery assets so that the clean electricity they produce does not go to waste.

Energy systems based on solar, wind, and batteries will also enable poorer countries and communities to close poverty and equity gaps by leapfrogging over previous barriers to human development. Unlike fossil fuels, nuclear power, or even hydropower, it is possible to deploy solar power and batteries virtually anywhere at any scale, which will lead to the localization, decentralization, and democratization of energy worldwide. Indeed, the greater solar energy endowment in sub-tropical countries (which also includes some of the world's poorest countries) has the potential to be a powerful social and economic equalizer. The sooner any community, region, or nation adopts solar, wind, and batteries, the sooner they can level the playing field.

Wherever energy abundance goes, prosperity has always followed. So, while it is true that it takes energy to meet all other needs, there are two extraordinary implications that logically follow from that fact: 1) as energy gets cleaner, *so does everything else*; and 2) as energy gets cheaper, *so does everything else*. The energy disruption will therefore help lift billions of people out of poverty and into prosperity.

The transportation disruption

At the time of this writing, the transportation sector accounts for about 16% of greenhouse gas emissions worldwide, and 29% of emissions in the United States.[48,66] The overwhelming majority of these emissions – more than 75% – come from internal combustion engine road vehicles that burn gasoline and diesel fuel.[67] These combustion engine cars and trucks will be disrupted by electric vehicles whose motors and batteries burn no fuels and therefore produce no emissions.

Electric vehicles were initially introduced alongside combustion engine vehicles around the turn of the 20th Century, but their real limitation since then has been battery technology. Gasoline, diesel, kerosene, and other hydrocarbon fuels contain a large amount of energy in a small mass, and up until recently we simply could not store enough energy in chemical batteries to compete with these fuels. As a result, we were unable to give electric vehicles a range comparable to their combustion engine counterparts. That has finally changed. Thanks to lithium-ion battery technology co-developed for use in electronics like smartphones and laptop computers, electric vehicles now have adequate range at an affordable price, and this will only increase as battery technology continues to improve. We saw in Figure 17 that battery costs have plummeted over the last decade, and are continuing to fall. As a result, the adoption of electric vehicles is now skyrocketing.

Figure 21: The disruption of transportation.

Adoption of electric vehicles (light-duty vehicles units sold) – global.

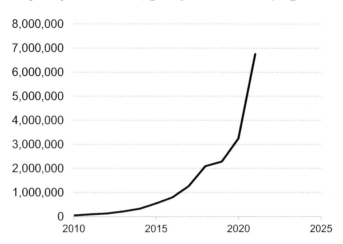

Source: RethinkX, 2022.[2]

As with energy, the reality of the transportation disruption is simple: the old technologies cannot compete economically with the new ones. By the late 2020s, virtually all new cars and trucks produced will be electric, as the powerful feedback loops driven by economic and social forces we examined in Chapter 3 will cause demand for combustion engine vehicles to collapse. At the same time, autonomous (self-driving) vehicles will transform our road transportation system, slashing the cost of travel per mile for both passengers and goods, and changing where we live and work along with how we organize our cities.

Electric vehicles require no fuel, need far less maintenance, and last much longer than combustion vehicles. This will slash the cost per mile over the life of the vehicle in applications like taxis where vehicles are in service most of the day. In addition, autonomous driving technology will then remove labor from the equation, reducing the cost per mile even further. As the utility of old vehicles relying on fossil fuels and a human driver rapidly approaches zero, many people and businesses will stop owning vehicles altogether, instead switching to transportation-as-a-service (TaaS) from public or private fleets. In dense urban areas, far-sighted societies might also choose to invest in undergrounding much of their road transportation in tunnels, which would combine the best benefits of personal transportation (privacy, safety, health/hygiene, 24/7 service, and door-to-door convenience) with those of mass transit (smaller per-passenger footprint and less traffic congestion).

Aviation accounts for only about 2% of global emissions, but will nevertheless be disrupted by electrification. Batteries still need to improve a great deal before they can store enough energy to provide a direct substitute for fuels on long flights, but we are likely to see such capability emerge in the 2030s. For short flights, however, the disruption will begin in the 2020s. Dozens of startup companies already have electric aircraft in advanced stages of development in anticipation of improving battery technology, including small designs capable of taking off and landing vertically the same way that helicopters do. Moreover, trips overnight in sleep-capable cars, vans, and buses that can drive themselves will provide an attractive alternative to air travel for distances of less than about 600 kilometers.

Shipping also makes up only about 2% of global emissions, and although there will be some direct disruption by the electrification of ships, the greater disruptive impact is likely to be indirect via reduction in shipping demand. This is because more than half of all freight is comprised of crude oil, oil products, coal, natural gas, iron ore, steel, automobiles, animal feed, livestock, and seafood – all of which will see demand plummet as a result of the combined effects of the energy, transportation, and food disruptions.[68]

The transportation disruption will enable poorer countries and communities to close poverty and equity gaps by increasing access to transportation, as well as by reducing the impacts of air pollution from combustion engine vehicles. And as with energy, wherever cheap transportation is readily available, prosperity has always followed. This means the same key implications of the energy disruption also logically follow for the transportation disruption: 1) as transportation gets cleaner, *so does everything else*; and 2) as transportation gets cheaper, *so does everything else*. The transportation disruption, especially in conjunction with the energy disruption, will therefore help lift billions out of poverty and into prosperity.

The food disruption

At the time of this writing, food and agriculture account for about 18% of greenhouse gas emissions worldwide. Of those emissions, over half are directly attributable to livestock, their manure, the crops raised to feed them, and the land deforested for their pasture and feed cropland. This means that nearly 10% of global emissions come from meat, dairy, eggs, and seafood.[48] These emissions are in addition to the fossil fuels we use in agriculture-related and seafood-related energy and transportation.

The food disruption will be driven by the economics of precision fermentation and cellular agriculture, which will compete with animal products of all kinds. My team's research found that precision fermentation will make protein production 5 times cheaper than from existing animal sources by 2030, and 10 times cheaper by 2035. The extraordinary precision with which proteins and other complex organic molecules will be produced also means that foods made with them will be higher quality, safer, more consistent, and available in a far wider variety than the animal-derived products they replace. Similarly, by the 2030s cellular agriculture will make meat, leather, and other products from cells in the laboratory much more cheaply and at a higher level of quality, safety, and consistency than the traditional animal products they replace.

The reason why precision fermentation and cellular agriculture can be so much cheaper while at the same time outperforming animal products in every respect is because they are inherently so much more efficient. Compared to livestock, the new technologies will be up to 10 times more water efficient, 10-25 times more input efficient, up to 20 times more time efficient, and up to 100 times more land efficient.[50]

The food disruption lags behind the energy and transportation disruptions by perhaps five years or so, but we can already see evidence for the beginning of the disruption in the data.

Figure 22: The disruption of food.

Cost of precision fermentation ($ per kilogram).

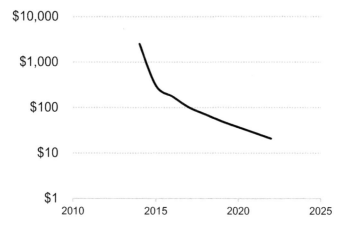

Source: RethinkX, 2022.

Cost of cellular agriculture ($ per kilogram).

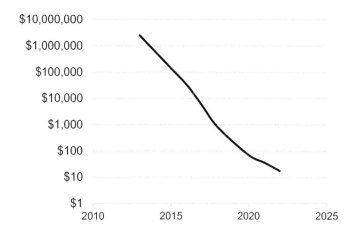

Source: RethinkX, 2022.

The economic competitiveness of products made with precision fermentation and cellular agriculture will be overwhelming. Cattle are particularly vulnerable because they are one of the least efficient parts of the industrial livestock system, which means they will be the first to feel the full force of the disruption. Beef and dairy businesses already operate with razor-thin margins and frequently require subsidies and other support to weather tough times. The disruption of the ground meat and dairy markets are just beginning, and adoption will tip and accelerate exponentially once cost parity is reached. Mounting competition from these technologies will therefore push the cattle industry over the brink into bankruptcy with a swiftness that will seem shocking to outside observers. All other commercial livestock industries worldwide will then quickly follow the same fate, as will commercial fisheries and aquaculture.

Perhaps the most astonishing environmental implication of the food disruption will be the staggering amount of land freed up from animal agriculture. It is easy to forget that agriculture has the largest footprint on the Earth's land surface of any human activity by far. We use about 40 times more land for farms, pasture, and grazing than we use for all mining, roads, buildings, parking lots, railroads, airports, and other built-environment infrastructure put together. And of the 5.1 billion hectares of total land we devote to agriculture, 3.3 billion hectares are used solely to support livestock.[69] The food disruption will free up about 80% of that land. This astounding implication deserves special emphasis:

The food disruption will free up roughly 2.7 billion hectares of land from animal agriculture – an area the size of the United States, China, and Australia combined.

All of that freed up land will offer an entirely unprecedented opportunity not only for fighting climate change but for conservation, reforestation, and rewilding as well. My team's research found that even without active efforts to maximize the rate of reforestation, the passive reforestation of these 2.7 billion hectares through natural recovery processes alone will capture and store a quantity of carbon equivalent to up to 20% of today's global emissions each year, on average, over the course of the century.[2]

In the oceans, the impact of the food disruption will also be extraordinary. Today there are over 4.5 million commercial fishing vessels in operation.[70] Commercial fisheries are poorly regulated and have devastated marine ecosystems worldwide, but recent research suggests that recovery can happen quite quickly once the destruction is halted.[71] The food disruption will decimate commercial fisheries worldwide, again because the cost, quality, consistency, and safety of precision fermentation and cellular agriculture products will make them overwhelmingly competitive against conventional seafood.

When I present this information in lectures and interviews, this is usually the point in the discussion where listeners ask whether anyone will actually be willing to buy precision fermentation and cellular agriculture products. But although skepticism of new technology is to be expected in the early days, history shows that this never lasts. Early precision fermentation and cellular agriculture products such as the Impossible Burger are already being well received. And it is worth remembering that we turn a blind eye to industrial livestock operations today, which are often nightmarishly cruel and unhygienic, and are themselves a very long way from 'natural'. The sanitary conditions alone in a precision fermentation brewery or a cellular agriculture lab will be a stark improvement compared to the conditions in which conventional meat and dairy products are produced.

Like the energy and transportation disruptions, the food disruption will also enable poorer countries and communities to close poverty and equity gaps by allowing the decentralization and localization of food production, as well as by reducing the impacts of air, water, and soil pollution from livestock. Precision fermentation and cellular agriculture facilities can be located in or close to towns and cities just as breweries are today, and this will have the additional benefit of making food systems more resilient worldwide, and thus reducing the vulnerability of poorer communities to the vagaries of global trade. The food disruption, especially in conjunction with the energy and transportation disruptions, will therefore help lift billions out of poverty and into prosperity.

Climate restoration: withdrawing carbon from the atmosphere and oceans

Over the last 200 years, humanity has emitted over 2 trillion tons of CO_2 and CO_2-equivalent greenhouse gases into the atmosphere, much of which has been absorbed by the oceans, and this has caused both climate change and ocean acidification.[56] In order to restore the atmosphere and oceans to a safe and stable condition, we will need to withdraw a substantial portion of those historical emissions. Estimates vary, but it is reasonable to expect that the necessary amount of carbon withdrawal (which also goes by the terms *carbon dioxide removal*, *negative emissions*, and *carbon drawdown*) will be somewhere between 500 billion and 1 trillion tons. This is a truly enormous amount of material, and a daunting challenge by any conceivable measure. So daunting, in fact, that much of the scientific and policymaking communities have considered it impossible for all practical purposes up until very recently.

To give a sense of scale, 1 billion tons of water is a cubic kilometer of water. That is a cube 1,000 meters on a side – almost three times the height of the Empire State Building. And we must withdraw at least 500 such cubes' worth of carbon from the atmosphere over the next several decades in order to truly solve climate change. Intimidating as this quantity of material may seem, keep in mind that we currently mine, dig, or otherwise extract about 50 billion tons of inorganic material worldwide each year already – roughly 40 billion tons of sand and gravel, 7 billion tons of coal, 3 billion tons of iron ore, and 0.5 billion tons of other metal ores and minerals. Thus, if we were to match the world's mineral extractive capacity with carbon withdrawal capacity of 50 billion tons per year, we could get the climate restoration job done in a single decade.

The reason why we don't already do this today is because it would be prohibitively expensive. A wide variety of carbon withdrawal methods have been proposed, from capturing and sequestering CO_2 when producing energy from biofuels (known as BECCS) to direct capture of CO_2 from the air.[72] But two options stand out as much more feasible than the rest because they are existing natural processes that can be directly amplified by the disruptions of energy, transportation, food, and labor.

The first of these carbon withdrawal options is reforestation. The good news is that reforestation is almost certainly the safest and cheapest option for pulling billions of tons of carbon out of the atmosphere (and therefore also from the oceans, thanks to the gas exchange between the two). Forests store carbon in the biomass of trees, plants, animals, and microorganisms above ground as well as below ground in roots and soil. As long as a forest remains standing, this storage is effectively permanent. And the even better news is that the food disruption will free up more land for reforestation than most environmental scientists and activists have ever dared to imagine possible. My team's research shows that reforestation alone can withdraw as much as 10 billion tons of carbon per year from 2035 onward, if we commit to actively managing and optimizing the process. The bad news, however, is that 10 billion tons per year is probably a hard limit, and the rate also eventually slows as forest growth maxes out over several decades, which means that reforestation alone is not enough.

In order to increase the total rate of carbon withdrawal to 25 billion tons per year by 2050, which would allow us to withdraw 500 billion tons of carbon from the atmosphere and oceans in two decades and thus restore them to a safe state before 2070, we need a second affordable option in addition to reforestation. My team's research indicates that the next most feasible option proposed so far is *ocean alkalinity enhancement* or OAE. This is a very fancy way of saying "grind up rocks into fine sand and dump them in the ocean". More specifically, OAE involves mining and crushing silicate rocks such as olivine, pyroxene, and serpentine into fine sand and dust in order to hugely accelerate the natural weathering process that these commonly-occurring minerals already experience on land as they are eroded by rain and rivers and washed out to sea. In seawater, the sand and dust undergo a complex series of chemical reactions and biological activity that ultimately converts the silicate compounds into carbonate compounds, thus capturing and permanently storing carbon as minerals in ocean sediment.[xxiii] This removes CO_2 from the oceans, which in turn then pulls CO_2 from the atmosphere via gas exchange, thereby helping to reverse the damage caused by greenhouse gas emissions.[73,74]

There are a number of other high-tech approaches to carbon withdrawal that have potential to play a role as well, but these all require a great deal more research and development before we can properly assess their cost and effectiveness. Some of these approaches may prove to be even more effective than reforestation and OAE. But for now, reforestation and OAE are low-tech, low-risk approaches to carbon withdrawal. (Planting trees and smashing rocks are things we humans have known how to do for a very long time). All we need to do is deploy them. But both methods are energy and labor intensive, and so scaling to the gigaton level is the hard part. It follows, however, that both reforestation and OAE will benefit enormously from superabundant, cheap, clean energy and transportation, as well as the eventual automation of vehicles and human labor. My team's research indicates that after the disruptions are complete, the cost of carbon withdrawal at scale could fall below $10 per ton, and possibly be as low as $1 per ton under some conditions.

Spread across 20 years, the cost of climate restoration could be as little as $50 billion per year. Although that is not an insignificant amount of money, it is certainly affordable for our civilization as a whole, and in any case saving the planet from climate catastrophe would be a bargain even at ten times that price.

How can we solve climate change?

The way to fully solve climate change is by following the 3-step recipe for success we discussed in Chapter 1:

1. *Innovation*: develop better technology and switch to it when it becomes economically competitive.
2. *Mitigation*: use that technology to reduce ongoing environmental damage.
3. *Restoration*: use that technology to repair past environmental damage.

The clean technologies driving the disruption of energy, transportation, and food already exist today and are in the process of being deployed and scaled up. We have seen how these technologies can reduce ongoing emissions. And we have seen how these same technologies will be instrumental in making large-scale carbon withdrawal feasible. The disruption of labor by AI, automation, and robotics will then follow, turning an already extraordinary transformation into a mind-bending one. Together, the four disruptions offer a truly complete solution to climate change that encompasses the restoration challenge as well as the mitigation challenge.

As climate change is the greatest environmental challenge of our time, let me draw specific attention to several key takeaway points:

1. **The way to solve climate change is through prosperity, not austerity.**

Energy, transportation, and food account for 90% of all global emissions. We cannot solve climate change by producing and consuming *less* energy, transportation, and food, just as we cannot save a burning building by putting out *some* of the flames. We can only solve climate change with *clean* energy, transportation, and food. Of course, we should always strive to be less wasteful, that goes without saying. But the idea that cutting back, tightening our belts, lifestyle changes, and otherwise imposing austerity measures across the economy and society will solve climate change is nonsensical. It cannot work even in principle, let alone in practice. Moreover, the social harms of austerity policies that reduce standards of living and impede human development – the burden of which would fall hardest on those communities and nations that are already disadvantaged – would be no less of a disaster than climate change itself. Although it might at first seem unintuitive, economic contraction would not help mitigate climate change, but would in fact do precisely the opposite: it would hamper our emissions reduction efforts by slowing down the disruptions of the energy, transportation, food, and labor sectors. Instead, the best way for governments, companies, organizations, and individuals to help solve climate change is to focus on accelerating the four disruptions.

2. We can achieve net zero emissions much more quickly than is widely imagined by deploying and scaling the technology we already have.

The technologies we need to achieve net zero emissions are science fact, not science fiction. We don't need to spend another 30 years and tens of billions of dollars on R&D to develop fusion power or room-temperature superconductors before we start to solve climate change. The task now is to deploy and scale existing clean technologies as fast as possible: solar PV, wind power, and batteries in the energy sector; electric vehicles, autonomous driving, and ride hailing in the transportation sector; and precision fermentation and cellular agriculture in the food sector.

3. The immense power of markets can now do the heavy lifting in mitigating emissions.

We have seen that the reason disruptions happen in the first place is because new technologies emerge which are cheaper and better, and thus outperform and outcompete the older ones. Because the disruptive technologies we need to solve climate change are all near or past the tipping point of becoming cost competitive, we now have market forces working *for* the environment rather than against it. This is extremely good news because decarbonization driven by market forces will work far better than any attempt by the world's nearly 200 governments to all successfully enact and enforce restrictions on either the supply or the demand side of the economy. It also means that the transformation will be swift, because throughout history disruptions driven by economic forces have tended to run their course in just 15 to 20 years.

4. A focused approach to solving climate change is better than an all-of-the-above approach.

The evidence to date strongly suggests that it is counterproductive for societies to divide their time, attention, and resources among a large number of different emissions reduction strategies. So far, this all-of-the-above approach has neither gained widespread social and political support worldwide, nor produced meaningful results. History and common sense clearly indicate that a much more effective approach is to concentrate on a single strategy rather than spreading ourselves thin with mediocre efforts across a dozen different fronts in hopes that they will sum up to something significant. The crux here is that up until now, no such strategy has been available. Disruptions changes the game. From now on, the single strategy we should focus on is simple: deploy and scale the disruptive clean technologies in the energy, transportation, and food sectors as quickly as possible.

5. The same technologies that allow us to mitigate emissions will also enable us to withdraw carbon dioxide from the atmosphere affordably.

Achieving net zero emissions is only the first step toward solving climate change. We must also return the composition of the atmosphere and oceans to safe levels. Up until now, the scope and cost of climate restoration have seemed overwhelming, and as a result the climate science community has made a concerted effort to avoid the topic. But the same technologies that will disrupt energy, transportation, food, and labor will also drastically reduce the cost of carbon withdrawal. Carbon withdrawal methods are all costly today because of their energy, vehicle (machinery), and labor requirements. These will become much more affordable thanks to superabundant clean energy, electric vehicles and machinery which run on that clean energy, and AI that automates those vehicles and machines. Reforestation and ocean alkalinity enhancement are likely our two best options at present, and the cost to withdraw carbon using these methods could fall below $10 per ton before 2050, which would make comprehensive global climate restoration feasible.

6. Decarbonizing the global economy will not be costly, it will instead save trillions of dollars.

The belief that switching to clean energy, transportation, and food will be expensive is a widespread myth. It is true that the clean technologies driving the disruptions were expensive in the past, but this is no longer the case today. To the contrary, these technologies will slash the cost of energy, transportation, and food by the 2030s – and all other goods and services across the global economy along with them. The reason disruption happens in the first place is because the new technologies are cheaper and more competitive, and so these three disruptions will naturally save us trillions of dollars purely in avoided economic costs, *in addition* to eliminating trillions of dollars of externalized environmental and social costs from fossil fuels, combustion engine vehicles, and animal agriculture.

7.   Carbon taxes are no longer strictly necessary.

The belief that carbon taxes are necessary to reduce demand for the older, dirty technologies and increase demand for newer, clean ones is a widespread misconception. It is true that the technologies driving the disruptions were expensive in the past and therefore needed market interventions like carbon taxes in order to be competitive, but this is no longer the case today. The tide has turned, and although making polluters pay is a sound policy in general that could still be useful, the disruption of fossil fuels, combustion engine vehicles, and animal agriculture is now inevitable and so carbon taxes are no longer strictly necessary to solve climate change. Today, instituting carbon taxes could even backfire and end up doing more harm than good if they hinder overall economic prosperity without sufficiently turbocharging the disruptions to compensate.

This may be a bitter pill for we environmentalists to swallow, especially since part of the motivation behind carbon taxes is to bring polluters to justice through financial retribution. But given that the environmental community has very limited political capital, it would be far more rational at this point to spend that precious resource on accelerating the disruptions directly and securing other important but less sexy environmental protections, rather than on beating the dead horse of already-doomed industries.

8.   **The clean disruption of energy, transportation, and food will help reduce the disparities between wealthy and poor communities, and between the wealthiest and poorest countries.**

As part of his crusade for 'factfulness', Hans Rosling famously created the GapMinder organization to show that the idea of a gap between developed and undeveloped countries (or Global North and Global South) is an illusion.[21] Yes, there are still very wealthy and very poor countries, but it is not a binary situation with a large gap between the two. Rather, the vast majority of countries and people are now spread evenly throughout the middle ground between the two extremes, precisely because those that were previously poor have made such enormous social and economic progress over the last several decades. (Visit www.gapminder.org to see the data yourself).

The clean technologies driving the disruptions will accelerate human progress even further, and catapult the standards of living in poorer communities and countries upward by drastically reducing costs of living and expanding access to 21st Century amenities. Because energy, transportation, and food are foundational sectors of the global economy, they comprise an outsized share of the cost in virtually every industry's value chain. Moreover, these new technologies can be localized and decentralized, and will therefore transform geopolitical relations by upending the concentrated geographic advantages and disadvantages of the past. *Every* country in the subtropics and tropics will be the 'Saudi Arabia of solar power'. These technologies will also enable poorer communities and countries to expand their prosperity and converge with the standards of living in wealthier ones. Best of all, this boom in prosperity will not itself result in any rebound effect in greenhouse gas emissions because the growth in energy, transportation, and food consumption will be met using the new clean technologies themselves.

The four clean technology disruptions ahead of us will allow us to have our cake and eat it too: they will let us fully solve climate change while elevating human prosperity worldwide at the same time.

Chapter 4 Notes

xvii Carbon withdrawal should not be confused with *carbon capture and storage* (CCS). CCS is industry jargon for capturing the emissions from coal and gas power plants and other point-sources of emissions. Attempts at 'clean coal' using CCS at old power stations have proven both technically challenging and financially infeasible in the past. This technology places an additional cost burden upon coal power plants that are already finding it impossible to compete with solar, wind, and batters. CCS has no hope whatsoever of being economically competitive compared to the new, clean technologies.

xviii Data are for installed capacity capex of utility-scale fixed-tilt monocrystalline solar photovoltaic panels.

xix Data are for installed capacity capex of utility-scale onshore wind power.

xx Data are for kilowatt-hours of battery energy storage at the pack level.

xxi Policymakers, investors, civic leaders, and the general public are also under the false impression that solar PV and wind power cannot supply 100% of electricity without weeks' worth of battery energy storage. This is because conventional models fail to recognize that future solar and wind generating capacity will greatly exceed the total electricity generating capacity installed today. My team's research shows that when the mix of solar, wind, and battery capacity is optimized, 100% solar, wind, and batteries systems are not only feasible but by 2030 will be by far the cheapest available option, both for any new power plant project, and in many cases compared to the cost of continuing to operate existing conventional power plants as well.

xxii Authors such as Tony Seba, Jeremy Rifkin, and Peter Diamandis have written at length about the significance of near-zero marginal cost energy abundance over the last decade.

xxiii It is important to recognize that OAE could have local ecological side effects – some negative, some positive. These need to be carefully assessed, even if on balance the benefit to the world's oceans would be overwhelmingly to the good.

CHAPTER 5

SOLVING TERRESTRIAL ECOSYSTEM DEGRADATION

"The best time to plant a tree is twenty years ago.
The second-best time is now."

– proverb

Terrestrial ecosystems across the planet have been badly degraded by human activity over the last several centuries. Key environmental problems on land include deforestation, desertification, habitat fragmentation and loss, soil erosion and contamination, invasive species, biodiversity loss, and endangered species. All of these problems share a common root cause: humanity's footprint on the landscape and oceans has damaged or outright destroyed the life that previously thrived there.

Up until now, there have been two major obstacles to solving all of these problems of terrestrial ecosystem degradation: limited land availability and high cost. The best and indeed *only* way to overcome those obstacles and actually solve these problems is to follow the same 3-step recipe for success we applied to climate change:

1. *Innovation*: develop better technology and switch to it when it becomes economically competitive.

2. *Mitigation*: use that technology to reduce ongoing environmental damage.
3. *Restoration*: use that technology to repair past environmental damage.

The technologies in this case are the same ones driving the disruption of energy, transportation, food, and labor. However, the food disruption in particular will play the dominant role in solving problems of terrestrial ecosystem degradation.

The enormous footprint of animal agriculture today

Agriculture is by far the largest form of land use worldwide. Our farms, pastures, and rangelands cover over one-third of all the land surface of the planet. That fraction rises to fully *half* of all habitable land, once we exclude glaciers, deserts, bare rock, dunes, salt flats, and beaches. And this account of our agricultural footprint does not include forest sylviculture to produce timber and fiber.

It may come as a surprise to some readers that all other built-environment land use is little more than a rounding error in comparison to agriculture. All cities and suburban residential areas, all mining operations, all roads and railways and airports and other infrastructure, all golf courses and sports fields, all landfills – all of that area *combined* covers just 1% of the world's land surface. The footprint of agriculture is 35 times larger than the rest of the built environment put together. And, astonishingly, we devote more than 80% of all that agricultural land to raising livestock. The total footprint of animal agriculture is 3.4 billion hectares – an area the size of North America, Central America, and South America combined. Most of that footprint is pasture and grazing land, but we also grow crops for animals, and this feed cropland covers about 540 million hectares – an area 10 times the size of France.

So, although non-agricultural land use does contribute to problems of terrestrial ecosystem degradation, it is no exaggeration to say that these other sources of impact are largely insignificant next to the footprint of animal agriculture. Suburban sprawl, mining, landfills, and infrastructure like roads and power lines are of course still cause for concern, but proportionally speaking they deserve only about 5% of our attention. The other 95% of our attention should be focused on animal agriculture.

Up until now, the only way that most environmental scientists, policymakers, and activists have been able to imagine we might reduce the footprint of animal agriculture is by changing our individual lifestyles and consuming fewer animal products. The conventional narrative therefore calls for each of us to eat less meat, and especially less beef and dairy – and to even become an outright vegetarian or vegan if we can. But this strategy has been an abject failure. So far, overall global demand for animal products has only increased over time, especially as growing economic prosperity in previously poorer countries like China has given people the choice to eat meat.[75]

A number of studies in recent years have shown the tremendous environmental benefits that we would see if everyone on the planet stopped consuming animal products.[76] But this has only ever been wishful thinking – until now.

Going vegan without going vegan

Precision fermentation and cellular agriculture technologies are no longer science fiction. Dozens of products are already commercially available, and costs are falling fast while at the same time quality and variety are improving by the day. Because the new technology is inherently so much more efficient than animal agriculture, precision fermentation and cellular agriculture products will become much cheaper than conventional meat, dairy, and other products within just a few years as the new industries scale up globally. As long as their quality equals or exceeds that of traditional products (and we have every reason to believe it will), then disruption is inevitable.

Animal agriculture is especially vulnerable to disruption because livestock industries around the world tend to operate at very low margins while at the same time depending on multiple revenue streams. Raising cattle, for example, is a risky enterprise at the best of times. It is difficult to be profitable at all without operating at a large scale, and every part of the animal must be utilized in order for the industry as a whole to be viable. This means cows cannot be profitable at current prices if they are grown only for cuts of beef like steaks; the industry also depends on revenue streams from ground beef, dairy, leather, gelatin, bone meal, and even manure. If any one of these revenue streams were to dry up, the price to end consumers of the other products would have to increase to make up the difference. This translates into vulnerability to disruption because the new technologies only needs to replace a single one of those revenue streams to tip the old industry into a death spiral of rising costs, higher end-consumer prices, shrinking demand, and ultimately collapse. On top of this, we will begin to see mounting social pressure to stop consuming animal products once there are compelling precision fermentation and cellular agriculture alternatives available that deliver the same or higher quality at the same or lower cost. This is not to say that everyone worldwide will suddenly come to view animal agriculture as inhumane and unethical, but rather that turning a blind eye to animal suffering, as so many of us do today, will become increasingly less acceptable as the new technology rolls out, and this will only serve to accelerate the disruption even further.

We began domesticating macroscopic organisms for food almost 12,000 years ago, which marked the first Agricultural Revolution. Today, we are domesticating microorganisms and animal cells to produce food in what my research team calls the Second Domestication. And like the first great domestication, precision fermentation and cellular agriculture will disrupt not only food but also non-food animal products used in pharmaceuticals, cosmetics, and materials as well.

By replacing virtually *all* of the animal products we use with these new technologies, we will achieve a similar environmental result to everyone becoming vegan, but through progress and prosperity rather than through sacrifice and austerity. Small niche markets for authentic animal products will surely persist for those willing to pay a high premium and endure mounting social stigma, but these will be luxurious indulgences sold in tiny quantities rather than mass-produced commodities.

Ecological restoration through conservation, preservation, and rewilding

By freeing up billions of acres of land from animal agriculture, the food disruption will create opportunities for restoring terrestrial ecosystem integrity through conservation, preservation, and rewilding beyond anything that environmental scientists, policymakers, planners, and activists have ever dared imagine were possible.

Conservation means protecting ecological integrity *for* human use. This environmental ethic was famously championed by Gifford Pinchot in the late 19th Century, and places value on natural ecosystems primarily on the basis of their usefulness to human beings. Today we rely upon many kinds of ecosystem services, from the provision of food and fiber to the purification of air and water, and much else. Conservation aims to restore and protect ecosystems because they have instrumental value in meeting our needs.[23,77]

Preservation means protecting ecological integrity *from* human use. This environmental ethic was famously championed by John Muir, who disagreed with and debated his friend Pinchot on the merits of conservation versus preservation in the late 19th Century and early 20th Century.[78] Preservation values the living world for its own sake, and not merely for its utility in serving human needs, and therefore aims to set aside and protect both existing wilderness areas and previously-developed lands.

Rewilding goes a step further beyond preservation, and aims to actively rebuild the wilderness character of landscapes and recreate their past ecological structure. For land previously used for agriculture, this means doing more than simply protecting it from human use. For example, we might also carefully reintroduce plant and animal species in order to restore more biodiversity and ecological function than would occur if the landscape were merely left to slowly recover on its own. The active reintroduction of keystone species like wolves and beavers, as well as the expulsion of invasive species, are examples of some of the active aspects of rewilding.

Each of these three approaches to ecological restoration has its own set of ethics and values, and so there continue to be debates about their respective merits and risks. These debates are only likely to intensify as the staggering opportunities created by the food disruption become increasingly apparent.

How can we solve problems of terrestrial ecosystem degradation?

New technology.

That is not the conventional answer, but this is not a conventional environmental book. A more conventional way of answering the question would be to offer an exhaustive description of how we can deploy all of the different conservation, preservation, and rewilding practices in the ecological restoration toolbox. Indeed, those answers take up entire textbooks because there is no simple one-size-fits-all approach to ecological restoration that works everywhere, given the enormous cultural and geographic variation across the globe.[79–82] But up until now, conventional proposals have always sidestepped the real heart of the problem, which is *where* to do all of the ecological restoration work and how to *pay* for it.

New technology is the better answer because it will allow us to overcome the two major obstacles – limited land availability and high cost – that for so long have stood in the way of actually solving deforestation, desertification, habitat fragmentation and loss, soil erosion and contamination, invasive species, biodiversity loss, and endangered species. To be sure, ecological restoration can be done well or poorly, and so it is crucial that we apply the best scientific knowledge to redressing each specific form of terrestrial ecosystem degradation. But lack of scientific knowledge is not what has prevented us from tackling these problems up until now. Rather, it has been a lack of opportunity and feasibility that have held us back. The upcoming technology disruptions change that picture completely.

Regarding land availability, research by my team and others has shown that the disruption of food by precision fermentation and cellular agriculture, and the resulting collapse of industrial animal farming, will reduce the amount of land dedicated to agriculture worldwide by about 75% between now and 2040. We saw in Chapter 4 that this means the food disruption will free up an area the size of the United States, China, and Australia combined. This will be, by far, the largest and fastest transformation of land use in human history. The 2.7 billion hectares of land freed up by the food disruption represent an unprecedented opportunity to both stop harming and start healing the world's terrestrial ecosystems.

Regarding cost, the disruptions of energy, transportation, and human labor will make the hard work of physically removing agricultural infrastructure, planting trees and other vegetation, reintroducing native species and expelling invasives, and monitoring progress along the way and afterwards easier, cleaner, and much, much cheaper.

Maximizing benefits and minimizing harms

As we saw in Chapter 1, simple does not mean easy. Although the end of animal agriculture will create opportunities for ecological restoration that we environmentalists could only dream of in the past, implementing solutions will still be difficult. There will be fierce disagreement about what to do with the bounty of newly-available land. Adapting to radical technological change is hard under the best of circumstances, and in the case of the food disruption many millions of people will lose their livelihoods as animal agriculture collapses. Agricultural practices are also deeply connected to traditions, identity, and culture. And the land itself is of course owned by individuals, families, communities, corporations, and governments – all with different values and priorities. Not everyone will be happy to say goodbye to a way of life that has persisted and helped define us for millennia. It is therefore crucial that we recognize and have compassion for the economic hardship and social turmoil that the food disruption will cause, even if it is temporary, and even if ending animal agriculture is clearly for the best in the long run.

It is also important to remember that the historical conversion of land to agricultural use has itself often been unjust. Indigenous peoples in particular have often been marginalized and expelled from their lands against their will by commercial and political forces beyond their control in the drive to expand and modernize agriculture. We must take great care to ensure that similar injustices do not occur as land use shifts again. In fact, the food disruption offers an extraordinary opportunity to rectify some of those past injustices by returning lands to their former indigenous inhabitants. Moreover, indigenous peoples often possess a deep cultural understanding of ecological integrity and stewardship, and so we should strive to combine ecological restoration with social equity and local knowledge wherever possible.

What now?

Disruption is coming and cannot be stopped. One of our most pressing challenges is therefore to plan *now* for how to best structure and incentivize the constructive repurposing of billions of hectares of agricultural land across the globe. Regardless of which approaches the world's societies choose to adopt, it is going to require a mix of individual initiative, social pressure, political will, and economic resources to undertake effective ecological restoration.

One of the most important things we scientists, policymakers, civic leaders, investors, and activists can do today to solve environmental problems associated with terrestrial ecosystem degradation is help society *get ready*, especially for the food disruption, so that when the time comes we can make the most of the incredible opportunities to heal our landscapes that lie ahead.

CHAPTER 6

SOLVING MARINE ECOSYSTEM DEGRADATION

"The Sea, once it casts its spell, holds one in its net of wonder forever."

— Jacques Yves-Cousteau

Marine ecosystems across the planet have been badly degraded by human activity over the last century. Key environmental problems in the world's oceans include overfishing, coral bleaching, eutrophication and hypoxic dead zones, ocean acidification, plastic pollution, habitat fragmentation and destruction, biodiversity loss, and endangered species. All of these problems are the result of our footprint on the oceans, which has damaged or outright destroyed the life that previously thrived there.

As with terrestrial ecosystem degradation, the only viable way to solve these problems is to follow the same 3-step recipe for success we applied to climate change:

1. *Innovation*: develop better technology and switch to it when it becomes economically competitive.
2. *Mitigation*: use that technology to reduce ongoing environmental damage.

3. *Restoration*: use that technology to repair past environmental damage.

The technologies in this case are the same ones driving the disruption of energy, transportation, food, and labor. However, as was the case with terrestrial ecosystem degradation, the food disruption in particular will play the dominant role in solving problems of marine ecosystem degradation.

The enormous footprint of commercial fisheries today

Commercial fisheries are the largest single source of harm to the world's oceans. Nearly 4.5 million fishing vessels ply the seas, from small skiffs with outboard engines to 500,000-ton factory ships longer than a football field. International waters are largely unprotected, and so the larger vessels travel many thousands of miles to reach the richest waters. Chinese commercial fisheries stand out as the largest culprit by far, with a fleet larger than the next top ten countries combined.

Nearly half of the world's target marine species are overfished, and virtually all of the rest are fully exploited. A number of once-abundant species, such as North Atlantic cod, have been decimated, and some such as the southern bluefin tuna are on the brink of extinction. In the process of pursuing target species, industrial fishing vessels can both capture other species unintentionally – known as bycatch – as well as damage the often-delicate coral and other ecosystems on the seafloor by dragging nets and anchoring indiscriminately. Investigative journalism has repeatedly shown that bycatch and other harms of commercial fisheries are grossly underreported.

Commercial fisheries also contribute substantially to marine pollution, with estimates ranging from 20% up to 50% of all plastic waste in the oceans coming from ghost gear and trash discarded by fishing vessels. These vessels also discharge fuels, industrial chemicals, and sewage indiscriminately into the water, and of course burn fossil fuels for energy which contributes to climate change and ocean acidification.

Regulations imposed on commercial fisheries are difficult to monitor and enforce, and so far have proven largely ineffective. What has worked quite well, however, is the establishment of large marine protected areas within the national waters of wealthy countries like the United States and Australia.

The footprint of agriculture and aquaculture on the oceans

Agriculture and aquaculture have a large footprint on the oceans in two important ways. The first is via commercial fisheries, because one third of all fish catch worldwide is used as animal feed for livestock and aquaculture.[83] The second is runoff from farms and onshore aquaculture ponds, which sends soil, fertilizers, and animal effluent down rivers and ultimately out into the sea. This nutrient enrichment, or eutrophication, can cause blooms of algae, and when the algae die they are decomposed by bacteria that consume the oxygen dissolved in the water. When oxygen levels fall too low to support large organisms like fish, the result is a hypoxic dead zone. Large areas of the Gulf of Mexico, for example, become hypoxic for part of the year as a result of agricultural runoff.

Going vegan (again) without going vegan

As with terrestrial ecosystem degradation, the only way that most environmental scientists, policymakers, and activists have been able to imagine we might reduce humanity's footprint on the oceans up until now is by changing our individual lifestyles and consuming fewer seafood products.

The conventional narrative therefore calls for each of us to eat less seafood, and to become an outright vegetarian or vegan if we can. But this strategy has failed. To date, global demand for seafood has only increased over time, driven in particular by growing economic prosperity in previously poorer countries like China.[75] But as we saw in the previous chapter, new technology offers a far more effective, reliable, and humane path to reducing seafood consumption.

At this time of writing, hundreds of start-up companies are aggressively developing precision fermentation and cellular agriculture technologies to replace a wide variety of seafood products, and the first commercial products are now available.[84] As expected, costs of these products are falling fast as the food disruption accelerates, while at the same time quality and variety are improving rapidly. Products made with the new technologies are inherently much more efficient than sailing thousands of miles across the oceans, sorting target species from bycatch, and processing (and usually freezing) the animals for further transport to their final destination. As a result, these new products will become much cheaper than conventional seafood within just a few years as the new industries scale up globally. As long as their quality equals or exceeds that of traditional seafood, which we have every reason expect, then complete disruption and the collapse of commercial fisheries and most aquaculture worldwide is inevitable before 2040.

As with animal agriculture, commercial fisheries are a low-margin industry that is dependent upon multiple revenue streams, and if any one of these revenue streams were to dry up, the price to end consumers of the other products would have to increase to make up the difference. If portions of the bycatch from tuna fisheries can no longer be sold as animal feed, for example, then the price of tuna will have to increase accordingly. This translates into vulnerability to disruption because precision fermentation and cellular agriculture only need to replace a single one of those revenue streams to tip the old industry into a death spiral of rising costs, higher end-consumer prices, shrinking demand, and ultimately collapse. And as with animal agriculture, we will begin to see mounting social pressure to stop consuming seafood once there are compelling new alternatives available that deliver the same or higher quality at equal or lower cost. We cannot expect everyone worldwide to suddenly come to view industrial-scale fishing as inhumane and unethical, but turning a blind eye to the destructive and inhumane aspects of commercial fisheries will become increasingly less acceptable as the new technologies roll out, and this will only serve to accelerate the disruption even further.

By replacing virtually all seafood with precision fermentation and cellular agriculture, we will achieve a similar environmental result to everyone becoming vegan, but through progress and prosperity rather than through sacrifice and austerity. Small niche markets for authentic seafood will surely persist for those willing to pay a high premium and endure mounting social stigma, but as with the disruption of animal agriculture on land, these will be relegated to luxurious indulgences whose environmental impacts are nominal.

Ecological restoration through conservation, preservation, and rewilding

Just like on land, the food disruption will remove the majority of humanity's ecological footprint from the world's oceans, offering us an opportunity to restore marine ecosystem integrity through conservation, preservation, and rewilding that exceeds anything that environmental scientists, policymakers, planners, and activists have ever dared imagine were possible.

We saw in the previous chapter that conservation, preservation, and rewilding are distinct environmental protection approaches that are based on different values and goals. Each of these has its own merits and risks, which their advocates will continue to debate. One crucial difference between marine and terrestrial ecosystems, however, is that the majority of the world's oceans are not owned by anyone, and so there is no equivalent of competing land use. This means that the end of commercial fisheries will naturally result in ecological restoration at an enormous scale, even without direct human assistance. Even better, new research conducted on marine protected areas has shown that marine ecosystems can recovery quite quickly if we just leave them alone for a while.[85]

How can we solve problems of marine ecosystem degradation?

New technology.

As in earlier chapters, this is not the conventional answer. But up until now, the more conventional answers have avoided tackling the real challenge, and instead have focused on how to reduce demand for seafood while making commercial fisheries 'sustainable'. Those proposals have not worked in the past, and are unlikely to work in the future, for reasons we have repeatedly discussed. Instead, new technology is the answer because it removes the underlying cause of the problem entirely. By analogy, this is like the difference between taking aspirin for a fever versus taking antibiotics to cure the underlying infection. And just like on land, ecological restoration in the oceans has not been constrained by lack of scientific knowledge, but rather by a lack of opportunity and feasibility. The upcoming technology disruptions change the game completely.

Here it is also important to note that ocean acidification is a major threat to the world's marine ecosystems that is not caused by overfishing, but rather by the same CO_2 emissions that cause climate change. When CO_2 levels in the atmosphere rise, more of the gas dissolves in seawater, which forms carbonic acid and lowers the pH of the oceans worldwide. As seawater becomes more acidic, marine organisms have more difficulty forming their shells with calcium carbonate, and this has the potential to trigger both gradual and sudden catastrophic changes in marine ecosystems. Like climate change, ocean acidification is a problem that won't just go away overnight once we stop using fossil fuels. And as we discussed at length in Chapter 4, halting CO_2 emissions is only the first step towards solving the problem – we will also need to withdraw hundreds of gigatons of carbon in order to fully heal the planet's oceans. We saw in Chapter 4 that deforestation and ocean alkalinity enhancement look like our best options, and that both will become vastly more feasible and affordable by the mid-2030s thanks to the combined effects of the energy, transportation, food, and labor disruptions.

A final threat to marine ecosystems that we have not discussed yet is plastic pollution, which we will cover along with other pollution and waste management problems in the next chapter.

What now?

Although the end of commercial fisheries opens the door to ecological restoration in the world's oceans at a scale that we environmentalists could only dream of in the past, we nevertheless still face a difficult road ahead. Many millions of people will lose their livelihoods as the global seafood and aquaculture industries collapse, and they will need more than just our compassion – they will need substantial social, political, and financial support as well. Like animal farming, fisheries practices are deeply connected to traditions, identity, and culture, and not everyone will be happy to say goodbye to a way of life that has persisted and helped define humanity for millennia.

Once again: disruption is coming and cannot be stopped. We must therefore have a plan in place for how best to adapt to the disruption of seafood and to deal with the economic hardship and social turmoil that follows. Ending commercial fisheries and aquaculture is clearly for the best in the long run, but the toll of human suffering along the way could be terrible for any society that is caught unprepared. Regardless of which approaches the world's nations choose to undertake, it is going to require a mix of individual initiative, social pressure, political will, and economic resources to provide a soft landing for the affected communities. And so, once again, one of the most important things we scientists, policymakers, civic leaders, investors, and activists can do today is help humanity *get ready* for the disruptions, so that we can maximize the benefits and minimize the harms along the way.

CHAPTER 7

SOLVING WASTE AND POLLUTION

"To make the world a better place, sometimes you have to pick up other people's trash."

– Bill Nye

Waste is an unwanted byproduct of any process that otherwise creates value. Not all waste is tangible or harmful, but when it is and we fail to properly dispose of it, we call it *pollution*. Whether or not waste warrants the label of pollution depends on its quantity, toxicity, persistence, and location. For most of human history, we didn't produce very much waste, and most of what we did produce was not terribly toxic or persistent. Moreover, it was almost entirely localized right around the areas where we lived. Today, however, the story is very different.

As for quantity, humanity now produces billion of tons of waste each year. Exact figures are difficult to obtain because consistent and reliable data are lacking for many countries, but in broad terms of mass and volume, most of human waste ends up in the air as exhaust gasses. This is because we mine and drill and pump nearly 10 billion tons of fossil fuels each year, the overwhelming majority of which we burn, which then emits greenhouse gases like carbon dioxide along with sulfur oxides, nitrogen oxides, carbon monoxide, and particulate matter made up of black carbon, metals and metallic compounds, and organic compounds. Of the several billion tons of solid waste we produce each year, most ends up in landfills, perhaps a quarter is burned, and less than a fifth is recycled. Probably less than 5% is actively littered, although the amount varies a great deal from one location to another, but that is still enough to send around 10 million tons of plastic pollution into the oceans each year.

As for toxicity, a significant fraction of our waste is hazardous to living things. We call acutely toxic substances that cause immediate harm *poisonous*, and humanity has understood poison as a concept for millennia. But it took us a much longer time to realize that substances can also be harmful in slow and subtle ways, and so it wasn't until the 20th Century that we came to properly appreciate chronic toxicity and understand the threat that pollution poses to long-term human and ecological health. For obvious reasons, we tend to put more time, effort, and resources into protecting ourselves and ecosystems from acutely toxic poisons than from chronically toxic pollutants whose effects don't become evident until years or decades after exposure. As ever, cost is the predominant consideration, and so the temptation to procrastinate and wait until 'later' to tackle the more insidious kinds of pollution whose harmful consequences don't fully materialize for many decades is strong even in societies that are wealthy enough to tackle the problem today. And in poorer communities and nations, addressing pollution is often unaffordable altogether.

As for persistence, the advancement of technology over the centuries has enabled us to create materials that are extremely durable. Durability is often a valuable property, but up until now we have tended to obtain and utilize that property in crude and indiscriminate ways. Materials like metal, glass, plastic, and cement are relatively primitive technologies because their properties are static. More advanced materials, which are now beginning to be developed in laboratories, will instead have dynamic properties that can be changed over time in a controlled manner. (Imagine a 'programmable' substance that could remain durable for years until commanded to abruptly biodegrade, for example). The crude durables of today have the potential to persist in the environment for hundreds, thousands, or even millions of years – often precisely because they do not occur naturally, and so no organisms have evolved to decompose them. This doesn't just include solids like metal, glass, plastic, and cement, but also liquids and gases. Thousands of toxic synthetic chemicals, for example, have the potential to persist in soil and groundwater for centuries.

As for location, our pollution now encompasses the globe. Whereas pre-modern pollution and runoff was once localized to settlements and their outskirts, today no ecosystem on the planet save for bacteria and archaea deep underground remain untouched by human waste. The substances we emit into the air spread quickly through the atmosphere, even those with a residence time of only days rather than centuries. Solid and liquid waste in surface waters and groundwater can travel great distances as well, especially once they reach the sea. Plastic trash discarded in a river on one side of the world can end up in an ocean garbage vortex on the other side of the world in just a few years.

Up until now, the ultimate obstacle that has prevented us from solving all problems associated with waste and pollution has been high cost. The best and indeed *only* way to overcome this obstacle is to follow the same 3-step recipe for success we applied to climate change, terrestrial ecosystem degradation, and marine ecosystem degradation:

1. *Innovation*: develop better technology and switch to it when it becomes economically competitive.
2. *Mitigation*: use that technology to reduce ongoing environmental damage.
3. *Restoration*: use that technology to repair past environmental damage.

The key technologies in this case are the same ones driving the disruption of energy, transportation, food, and labor. Each of these has a crucial role to play in bringing down the cost of waste reduction, management, and cleanup.

Waste reduction

Up until now, it has made good sense to focus on reducing waste and thus preventing pollution at the source. There are two very different ways to reduce waste, which align with the degrowth versus decoupling debate we discussed in Chapter 1.

The degrowth approach is to simply do *less* of whatever it is that generates waste in the first place. However, all of the harvesting, mining, manufacturing, assembling, distributing, and other forms of 'production' and concomitant 'consumption' that generate waste across the economy are also forms of *value creation*. These are not the only ways to create value, of course, but they are vital nonetheless. Unfortunately, curtailing economic activity therefore means creating less value by definition, and that creates problems – both pragmatically and ethically.

In pragmatic terms, economic activity is the lifeblood of our modern standard of living precisely because it creates so much value, and recessions and depressions serve as a warning for how harrowing the loss of collective material prosperity can be. Moreover, no politically plausible mechanisms have ever been proposed for how to enforce any significant curtailment of production and consumption at the national or international scale. If we genuinely wanted the global economy to contract to any real degree, we would need to force a permanent economic depression across all wealthy countries, while simultaneously prohibiting economic development in poorer countries – most especially those with large populations. It is hard to imagine how the entire world could agree on which policies and regulations to enact in order to achieve this, and even harder to imagine how they could be enforced. We have also seen that social stability and peace are reliable results of material prosperity, whereas social unrest and war are frequent if not inevitable results of material deprivation.[86] Indeed, the extraordinary and unprecedented global peace we have enjoyed for over 80 years (imperfect as it is) may well be due more to the enormous increase in material prosperity we have seen worldwide than to any sudden rise in humanity's wisdom during that time. Moreover, if economic depression were to trigger violent conflict, it is unlikely that waste reduction or other environmental protections would remain high on the list of priorities.

In ethical terms, choosing to curtail economic activity requires passing judgment on what forms of value creation are preferable to others, and that is very treacherous territory indeed. Who gets to decide what is valuable and what isn't? Sure, most of us would agree that the world would be better off without land mines, nuclear weapons, heroin, and for-profit health insurance. But beyond banning the most obvious offenders, we must be extremely cautious. After all, a large fraction of goods and services – perhaps the majority – are not strictly necessary. It may seem reasonable to ask whether anyone really needs a yacht or a sportscar, for example. But does anyone really need to drink beer, either? Or wear makeup or perfume? Or watch television and go to the movies? Or travel to other countries for vacation? Should we outlaw golf? Or scuba diving? Or owning pets? Should we limit the number of miles a person can travel? Or how many electronic devices they can own? It is impossible to know where to draw the line, and history has repeatedly shown us that prohibition is folly. Things go terribly wrong whenever societies try to dictate personal preferences and oppress individual choices, whether in the name of decency or piety or sustainability or anything else.

Because of these obstacles, the degrowth approach to reducing waste is not a workable solution. To cut overall waste by 50%, for example, we would need to cut economic activity by 50% *permanently*, and that alone would be an unmitigated catastrophe. For comparison, the Great Depression caused a 26% decrease in global economic activity as measured by GDP, and a 47% decrease in industrial output in the United States, between 1929 and 1933. The combination of economic downturn, unemployment, and deflation wreaked havoc worldwide, even though the Great Depression itself was centered in the United States at a time when global trade was far less interdependent than it is today. Recovery from the Great Depression was slow in many areas, and its crushing effects in Weimar Germany in the 1930s are widely held to be a key causal factor in the rise of the Nazi Party and World War II.[87] Even if societies managed to decide which forms of value creation to curtail and prohibit in an equitable way, and even if they also somehow managed to navigate a permanent 50% global economic contraction without succumbing to violent conflict, we would *still* only have reduced ongoing waste by half – and done nothing to clean up the messes we've already created. To return to the burning house analogy, we would have extinguished only half of the flames and done nothing to the repair the damage that has already occurred, while at the same time created a separate disaster as bad as or worse than the fire itself. It is like thinking that bulldozing half of your burning house is a 'sustainable' way to solve the problem.

Alternatively, the decoupling approach to reducing waste is to make various processes of value creation more efficient through technological innovation, so that less waste is generated per unit of value created. This makes good sense across many different forms of economic activity, but there is a snag: maximizing efficiency does not always align with minimizing cost, and so businesses are not always financially motivated to do so. It's often cheaper to just do a sloppy job of things and discard the waste, which is why many environmental regulations aim to increase the cost of waste with taxes, tariffs, and fines. The rationale here is that if we use the law to make generating waste expensive, companies will have incentive to become more efficient in order to save money. However, if those legally-imposed costs are high enough, businesses will also have strong incentive to lie and cheat about their waste and pollution, and so enforcing the law is a difficult – and expensive – challenge, especially in poorer communities and countries.

Indeed, disregard of existing environmental rules and regulations is already rampant in most poorer countries today.

This is where the disruptions of energy, transportation, food, and labor come in: they will dramatically lower the cost of reducing waste across the board. (We will return to the disruptions in detail toward the end of the chapter). At the same time, they will raise prosperity across the board, giving all societies and all communities greater means to shoulder whatever costs do remain.

Developing and deploying new technology to reduce waste is therefore a much more reasonable approach than degrowth, so long as we are careful to go about it the right way and recognize its limitations. While there is certainly scope for substantial improvements across most industries (in many cases, much more than 50%), we must be realistic and admit that zeroing out waste entirely across all production processes throughout the entire economy will not be achievable any time soon, nor can we ignore the waste we have already generated in the past that continues to impact human and ecological health today. Reducing waste and pollution at their source is a great idea, and using new technology to do is the right approach, but until we have technologies like the Star Trek replicator that can construct any physical object atom-by-atom in seconds without any waste at all, we will still have the challenge of waste management on our hands as well.

Waste management

Waste management is relatively straightforward, but collecting, sorting, recycling, and disposal are all expensive processes – *today*.

Collecting waste takes a lot of energy, labor, and capital in the form of hardware. This includes not just solid waste like what ends up in garbage bins, but liquid wastes like sewage and farm effluent, as well as waste gasses from industrial processes and burning fossil fuels.

Sorting waste once it has been collected also takes a lot of energy, labor, and hardware. As part of the environmental studies program we taught at UCLA, we used to take undergraduate students to visit facilities where municipal solid waste and recyclables are sorted by hand. It is some of the most miserable, grueling, dehumanizing work imaginable. Sorting liquids and gasses must be done by machinery, but those facilities are not much fun either. The sewage treatment plants of Los Angeles were another field trip destination for our students, and you can literally smell them from a mile away.

Recycling waste once it has been sorted takes even more energy, labor, and hardware. One of the most effective ways to utilize sorted waste – perhaps surprisingly – is to burn it for energy. When designed and operated properly, waste-to-energy incinerators can reduce waste to minimally hazardous ash while capturing all exhaust gases and generating electricity at the same time. Unfortunately, these high-tech facilities are also high-cost. Other recycling facilities can turn plastic, paper, glass, and metal waste streams back into new input feedstock for the same industries they came from, but these too are expensive to build and run properly, and as a result only a frustratingly small proportion of waste actually ends up being legitimately recycled.

Finally, disposing of waste that cannot be affordably recycled takes energy, labor, and capital in the form of both hardware and landfill area. There is no shortage of land in the world that is suitable for the comparatively tiny landfill requirements of our civilization as a whole (all of the solid waste generated worldwide each year would fit in a landfill area $1/100,000^{th}$ the size of the Sahara Desert). But not all land is equally accessible, and so waste must be transported from where it is produced to where it can be safely disposed of. For this reason, many cities export their garbage to other areas, and some smaller nations with large populations even export their garbage to other countries.

In principle, we could physically transform all of the waste we produce into either useful or at least harmless forms – with the possible exception of some radioactive wastes – if only it weren't for the high cost of doing so. The only reason why we allow waste to turn into air, water, or soil pollution is because waste management is expensive, and that is why wealthier communities and nations manage their waste better than poorer ones – they can *afford* to.

The upshot here is that if we could find a way to dramatically lower the cost of waste management, then humanity as a whole could afford to stop it from turning into pollution in the first place.

As with waste reduction and pollution prevention, this is where the disruptions of energy, transportation, food, and labor come in: they will dramatically lower the cost of waste management across the board, while at the same time raising overall prosperity as well, making industries and communities and entire nations far more likely to do the job and do it right.

Waste clean-up

There is a cynical old saying that "the solution to pollution is dilution". The bitter irony is that dilution is precisely what makes pollution so expensive to deal with. Picking up trash is relatively easy if it is all located in one place. But it is vastly more difficult when it is spread widely across the landscape, or suspended in thousands of square miles of ocean, or diffused throughout the planet's entire atmosphere. And the smaller the constituent pieces of trash are, the harder it is to gather them all up. This is what makes the challenge of withdrawing carbon from the atmosphere and oceans so formidable.

In purely physical terms, cleaning up pollution is a battle versus entropy. The second of law of thermodynamics works against us every step of the way, pushing any closed system towards disorder over time. The Earth, however, is *not* a closed system: we have the benefit of energy pouring in from the sun all day every day. And we can harness that energy – just as the biosphere does – to reverse entropy in our beautiful little corner of the universe. So, although the air and oceans and soils of the world all tend toward uniformly mixed slurries without biological or human intervention, we can indeed intervene to reorganize them by selectively removing the materials we judge ought not to be there. In principle, we could clean up every scrap and speck and molecule of pollution on the planet, if only it weren't for the prohibitively high cost of doing so.

In practical terms, the reason we don't keep every square inch of the landscape and every drop of water in the oceans as clean as a whistle is that it is prohibitively expensive to do so. At best, the communities around the globe that are wealthy and stable enough to undertake environmental cleanup tend to care only for their own backyards.

But this is about to change in a very big way, thanks to the four disruptions.

How can we solve problems of waste and pollution?

New technology.

Once again, this is not the conventional answer. A more conventional way of answering the question is to offer an exhaustive description of how we can deploy a wide variety of waste reduction and management and cleanup strategies across myriad different social, political, and geographic circumstances worldwide. Such answers are of course an essential part of the picture, and they take up entire textbooks because there is no simple one-size-fits-all approach to waste and pollution that works everywhere.[88–92] But this has always sidestepped the real heart of the problem, which is that dealing with waste and pollution has simply been *too expensive* up until now – especially for less prosperous (meaning poorer) communities and countries.

The solution is clear: we must lower the cost of waste and pollution prevention, management, and cleanup, while simultaneously increasing human prosperity, so that the push-pull combination of these two forces makes solving the problem affordable everywhere.

How can we do this? With the disruption of energy, transportation, food, and labor.

The energy disruption driven by solar, wind, and batteries will not only lower the financial cost of waste and pollution reduction, management, and cleanup by providing cheaper electricity, but it will of course clean up energy *itself* as well. This double-whammy will encompass *all* economic activity *everywhere*, because energy is an input into virtually every link in every supply chain of every industry. My research team's analysis suggests that the cost of energy could drop by 50-90%

because of the disruption, depending on the location and industry, and for some parts of the year the surplus energy from solar and wind (which we call *super power*) may even be free. These savings will cascade throughout the entire global economy.

The transportation disruption driven by electric vehicles will lower the financial cost of waste and pollution reduction, management, and cleanup for similar reasons. Like energy, transportation is an input into economic activity of all kinds, and today it is expensive and dirty. My research team's analysis suggests that the cost of transportation will fall by 90% or more because of the disruption, and as with energy these savings will cascade throughout the global economy.

The food disruption driven by precision fermentation and cellular agriculture will make solving the waste and pollution challenge easier, but for very different reasons. A huge amount of waste and pollution is produced as a direct result of animal agriculture and wild caught seafood. New technologies have and continue to be developed as Band Aid solutions to reduce the impacts of these old industries, such as feeding seaweed to cows to reduce their methane emissions and using LED lights on fishing nets to reduce inadvertent bycatch of sharks and rays.[93,94] But the new food technologies are different because they will wipe out animal agriculture and commercial fisheries altogether, taking their waste and pollution along with them. My team's research suggests that these industries will collapse to less than 5% of their current size before 2040. Meanwhile, we expect the new precision fermentation and cellular agriculture industry that rises in their place to generate only a tiny fraction of the waste of the older industries – certainly less than 10%, and possibly as little as 1%.

The labor disruption driven by automation will have a massive impact on waste and pollution reduction, management, and cleanup. In many production processes, for example, it is impossible to avoid generating a lot of waste in the first place because humans cannot perform tasks (say, cutting metal and wood, or applying paints and other finishes) fast enough or precisely enough or safely enough. Automated machinery will be able to do so far more easily. Collecting, sorting, recycling, and disposing of waste once it exists are all labor-intensive activities as well, the majority of which are readily amenable to automation. Cleaning up waste and pollution is very labor-intensive too, whether it is picking up litter off of beaches and roadsides by hand, or operating machinery and vehicles that scour and filter contaminants from air, water, and soil. Automating these cleanup tasks will therefore drastically increase their affordability. (There are additional forms of cleanup that we currently do not undertake which advanced robotics could render feasible, and we will cover these more speculative prospects in the last chapter, but for the discussion here we are only talking about automating existing forms of cleanup work).

As impactful as each of these disruptions will be in its own right, the real magic happens where they catalyze themselves and mutually reinforce one another. For example, it takes a lot of *energy* to make solar, wind, and batteries, so building out that capacity in turn makes it cheaper and cleaner to build *even more* capacity, in a feedback loop. The same autocatalytic or self-accelerating dynamic of applies to the other disruptions as they scale too: electric vehicles make it cheaper to build more electric vehicles, precision fermentation and cellular agriculture make it cheaper to produce more food, and automation makes it cheaper to do more automation. But even more spectacular are all of the interconnections between the disruptions that mean they will all accelerate one another as well. For example, it takes a lot of energy to make electric vehicles, and also a lot of transportation to build and deploy solar, wind, and batteries. The more you do of both, the cheaper and cleaner they each become. The same is true for every permutation among all four of the disruptions.

Taken together, the disruption of energy, transportation, food, and labor will radically lower of the cost of waste and pollution reduction, management, and cleanup. At the same time, they will lower the cost of *everything else* in the global economy as well, making all societies everywhere far more prosperous across the board. The push-pull combination of these two forces will in turn render waste and pollution reduction, management, and cleanup affordable enough to undertake everywhere without debate or compromise. And we won't have to wait a century for all of this to happen – we will be there by 2040.

What now?

Once again, disruption is coming and cannot be stopped, and so a key challenge is to plan *today* for how to best structure and incentivize waste and pollution reduction, management, and cleanup once the disruptions start to manifest. We scientists, policymakers, civic leaders, investors, and activists can help society *get ready*, so that when the time comes we can make the most of the incredible opportunities to stop harming and start healing our atmosphere, oceans, and landscapes that lie ahead.

CHAPTER 8

MAKING DECISIONS IN A CHANGING WORLD

*"It is change, continuing change, inevitable change, that is
the dominant factor in society today. No sensible decision
can be made any longer without taking into account not only
the world as it is, but the world as it will be."*

– Isaac Asimov

One of the questions my research team is asked most often is, what can we do to maximize the social, economic, and environmental benefits of technology disruptions while minimizing the harms? There is no one-size-fits-all answer to this question because so much depends on the particular details of the geographic region, community, or industry under consideration. Instead, we work with policymakers, investors, civic leaders, and other decisionmakers to find answers that make sense in their particular situation. Nevertheless, the specifics emerge from an analytical process that is guided by general principles, and so in this chapter we will examine those principles.

Principle 1: Be prepared.

Although it is simple and self-evident, being prepared is by far the most important step in successfully navigating disruption. Like any major system shock, disruptions will always seem much less like an opportunity and much more like a disaster for anyone caught by surprise, so the value of knowing what is coming in advance and getting ready for it is enormous.

Some forms of change are slow and steady, and only make a modest difference. Disruption is different. Disruption is, by definition, radical change that is abrupt, nonlinear, and profoundly impactful. In order to prepare for disruption, we must recognize the following:

- **The change that is coming is inevitable and cannot be stopped**

We have seen throughout the preceding chapters why the disruptions of energy, transportation, food, and labor are inevitable and cannot be stopped: the competitive advantages of the new technologies will simply be overwhelming. While it is true that incumbent industries have mounted successful campaigns in the past to slow down research and development of disruptive new technologies, as in the case of the fossil fuel industry and incumbent energy utilities in the United States working to delay solar photovoltaic technology, these efforts cease to be effective once a disruptive technology begins to deploy to market.[95] Indeed, they can even start to backfire once public support shifts away from the incumbents toward the new technologies, as we saw from Figure 10 in Chapter 3. Our focus at every level from individual households to industries to entire nations therefore needs to be on accepting the inevitability of change of bracing for impact.

- **The change that is coming will happen faster than most expect**

In nearly all historical examples, incumbents had far less time to respond to disruption than they presumed. Kodak, for example, owned a number of key digital camera technology patents and even offered digital cameras alongside their competitors when the disruption took off in the mid-1990s, but the company was far too slow to realize that film cameras were doomed and thus far too slow to fully commit to the digital future. As a result, they were steamrolled by their more innovative competitors who had less to lose and were thus willing to fully commit to the disruption with bold, decisive action. We are almost certain to see a similar pattern emerge over the next decade in the energy, transportation, and food sectors as the incumbent companies in the fossil fuel, automotive, animal farming, and seafood industries all react too slowly and without sufficient commitment to the disruptions they face.

- **The change that is coming will be transformative**

There is an important distinction between a technology substitution and a technology disruption. Compact fluorescent lights (CFLs) began to displace incandescent lightbulbs in the 1990s, but although CFLs are somewhat more efficient and longer lasting, they were merely a substitution for the older technology. By contrast, LED lightbulbs are a disruption because they dramatically outperform both incandescent and CFL bulbs – they are cheaper, safer, more efficient, more controllable, and can be made in a much wider range of sizes and form factors. As a result, LEDs have changed how we think about lighting more broadly and opened up entirely new product categories and business models. We now use LEDs in long strings, in flexible strips, on portable handheld devices, underwater, and in a wide variety of applications that were never possible with the previous technologies.[96]

Other disruptions have followed the same pattern, as we saw in Chapter 3. Electricity was not a simple substitution for whale oil, but instead created an entirely new energy system. Automobiles were not a simple substitution for horses, but instead created an entirely new transportation system. Farming was not a simple substitution for hunting and gathering, but instead created an entirely new food system. The difference between substitution and disruption is that substitution is simply a one-to-one replacement of existing products, services, and applications, whereas disruption transforms the underlying system itself and creates entirely new possibilities we might never have dreamed of before. The Internet disruption of information and communications is a recent example of this phenomenon.

Today's disruptions of energy, transportation, food, and labor will transform every facet of the global economy and much of how we currently organize society. The world of abundance they create will open up wholly new frontiers of possibility. What was science fiction yesterday is science fact today, and will be the new normal tomorrow.

- **The temptation to resist the change that is coming will be extremely strong**

For any sector, industry, or market facing disruption, clinging to the status quo is a losing strategy. Unfortunately, there are very few real examples of incumbents self-disrupting and wholly reinventing themselves.[97] In most cases, what we have seen instead is newcomers – usually distant outsiders – seizing the lion's share in the midst of disruption, building success on innovative new ideas, business models, and modes of organization.

Unless they embrace disruption, the winners of yesterday and today will be the losers of tomorrow. Size and market dominance offer no protection, and history has shown us again and again that even the most powerful incumbents can collapse with shocking swiftness. It can be difficult for both outside observers and insiders themselves to even imagine that failure is possible – as in the case of the fossil fuel industry, the combustion engine vehicle industry, or the livestock industry today. Many of the largest companies involved seem both too big to lose and too big to (be allowed to) fail. But in 2007 it was just as hard for anyone to imagine that Nokia, which controlled over 50% of global market share of smartphones and was worth more than $150 billion, would fall to just 3% market share six years later. In 1990 it was hard to imagine that film cameras would collapse from 100% of market share to less than 1% within 15 years and send Kodak, worth over $10 billion, into bankruptcy. In 1900 it was hard to imagine that combustion engine vehicles would end centuries of horse-based transportation, or that electric motors would help end millennia of child labor. And in 1440 it was hard to imagine how the printing press would wipe out the profession of scribes, together with the centuries-old control of information by organized religion.

But being forewarned is being forearmed, and now that we understand disruption better than ever before, it is possible for insiders and outsiders alike to prepare for change and position themselves to take advantages of the tremendous opportunities that lie ahead.

- **The change that is coming will be overwhelmingly positive**

We naturally fear the unknown, and so change can be frightening. It is therefore no surprise that we focus our attention on everything that could go wrong instead of everything that is sure to improve as a result of the energy, transportation, food, and labor disruptions. It doesn't help that media business models expressly target and reinforce our fears by focusing on all the bad news in the world – hence the old adage about newspaper headlines, "if it bleeds, it leads". But in order to prepare successfully for the change that is coming, we must make a disciplined effort to overcome our natural negativity biases.

The bottom line is that the four disruptions will make almost everything across the global economy and human civilization much cheaper and much cleaner. If making a high quality of life affordable for everyone and less harmful for the planet is not positive change, then what is?

The mistake so many of us make is to assume that the zero-sum, win-lose status quo cannot change, and that human prosperity must always come at a terrible cost to the rest of the natural world. By making this assumption, many of my fellow environmentalists fear the prospect of a huge increase in human prosperity because they assume it will mean a huge increase in our ecological footprint. But as we have seen throughout the previous chapters, this is no longer the case. The new, clean technologies are different this time, and the prosperity they will grant us is exactly what we need – not just to stop harming the world, but to begin actively healing it as well.

Preparing for positive change is entirely different than preparing for negative change. Hunkering down in the cave to wait out the storm is the wrong move here. A better analogy to our current situation is the disruption of information by the Internet: at every scale, from individuals to communities to industries to nations, we need to position ourselves, our attention, and our resources for the deluge of new opportunities that is barreling toward us.

Principle 2: Start experimenting.

It is extremely difficult to predict ahead of time exactly which new ways of doing things will be most successful following a major technology disruption. The dot-com boom and bust in the late 1990s is a good example, because it shows that although the potential of the Internet was quickly becoming obvious to everyone, it wasn't at all clear which specific new business models were going to succeed. The crucial lesson from this and other past examples of disruption is to start experimenting sooner rather than later. This can be difficult – and frightening – for communities, industries, and even entire cultures that are traditionally apprehensive about failure. Part of the formula for success of Silicon Valley culture is its tolerance for risk and failure, and this is a pattern that is worth emulating amidst disruption.

Principle 3: Learn and adapt in the race to the top.

The four disruptions have created a race to the top that touches virtually every aspect of society and the economy. The results of experimentation will lead to both successes and failures, and that means the more individuals, communities, regions, and countries that run experiments the better, because it gives us all more to learn from. The role of policymakers, investors, civic leaders, and other decisionmakers is to put this knowledge into action at every level in order to successfully adapt to the new reality created by disruption.

In general, this will mean withdrawing support from the doomed incumbent industries – including ending existing subsidies, breaking up existing monopolies, refusing to lock in long-term contracts, rejecting pleas to socialize losses, and salvaging any assets of value as the older businesses collapse. It will also mean investing aggressively in the new industries and their associated infrastructure, removing obstacles to deployment, rapidly developing and adopting new standards, and emphasizing transparency, stability, resilience, and agility every step of the way.

Principle 4: Protect people, not businesses or industries.

A pattern we see repeatedly throughout history is that incumbent businesses and industries will seek protection from disruption by turning to their governments. Protection can take the form of subsidies and handouts to the old industry, regulations and prohibitions that impede companies and industries forming around the new technology, and bailouts when the old industry collapses. Almost invariably, the benefits of these measures accrue not to the workers or communities whose livelihoods depend on the incumbent industry, but instead to a privileged few who own and control that industry's companies. The public should therefore anticipate these shenanigans, hold their governments to account, and prevent them from making this mistake. Instead of propping up doomed companies and industries, our governments should instead focus on helping the affected individuals and communities adapt to the disruption. Direct financial assistance, re-training, and other options should all be on the table. Here too there is no one-size-fits-all solution that will work everywhere for every disruption, and so preparation, experimentation, and learning are again essential.

One issue that central banks, governments, and investors will need to be especially well-prepared for is the potential for supply-side deflation across the economy caused by the disruptions. Just as there has been deflation in information technologies as the cost of computation, memory, and bandwidth has ceaselessly plummeted (and their supply increased) year after year, we will see parallel impacts across the economy as the costs of energy, transportation, food, and labor decline while their supply surges from scarcity towards superabundance – with cascading effects across all other industries as a result. Deflation driven by abundance (meaning by an increase in aggregate supply, not by a decrease in aggregate demand) need not necessarily be harmful to society, as the case of information technology itself illustrates, but decisionmakers will nevertheless need to plan around this transformation – and, in particular, around the greater risk of carrying debt under deflationary conditions.

Principle 5: Use disruption as an opportunity to rethink assumptions.

New technologies tend to have different and often much greater capabilities than older ones, and as a result they open up entirely new possibilities for an industry, sector, or the whole of society. Personal computers, for example, weren't just faster typewriters. They transformed the way we live and work on almost every level in almost every corner of society and the economy. The disruption of energy, transportation, food, and labor will do the same. System shocks of this kind are a good opportunity to revisit long-standing assumptions, to take stock of the status quo with fresh eyes, and to open our minds to the possibility of doing things very differently in the future than we have done in the past. The COVID-19 pandemic, for example, let us challenge the wisdom of working in an office in-person each day, and it now appears as though some amount of remote work may become part of the new normal.

Our world is about to change in extraordinary ways. If we are open-minded and prepared, we can use the upcoming disruptions as opportunities to rethink our assumptions and direct that change for the better. What could a world with superabundant, clean energy look like? How might we put superabundant, clean transportation to use improving both human and ecological wellbeing? How will we repurpose the billions of hectares of land we no longer need for animal agriculture? What are the possibilities in a world with an unlimited supply of labor provided by machines?

The sky is the limit, but to see it we need to look up.

CHAPTER 9

THE FUTURE OF ENVIRONMENTALISM

"Remember to look up at the stars and not down at your feet."

– Stephen Hawking

We all want a brighter future. For ourselves. For our children. For our family and friends and communities. For our planet.

The question is, how do we get there?

Many believe the only way is by going backward – by slowing down, retreating from the present, returning to the past. By decreasing, declining, degrowing. By *regress*.

This is wrong. Regress has never worked before and it won't work now. It will only make solving our existing problems harder, and it will create new problems in the meanwhile. It is time we consign this bankrupt idea to the dustbin of history.

The way to achieve a brighter future is to keep moving forward. To keep overcoming obstacles and solving problems. To keep imagining, innovating, and improving. To keep making *progress*.

What kind of future?

What does a *brighter* future actually mean? Is progress something we can even define, given that not everyone shares the same preferences?

Some people love the bustle and noise of cities and the clean geometric elegance of glass and chrome skyscrapers, while others love the country and the organic richness of rolling green hills and forested vistas. In Chapter 1, I mentioned that whenever I challenged my students at UCLA to resolve this dilemma they would always eventually reach the same compromise: *progress ought to maximize freedom of choice.*

A brighter future is one in which we expand our options, not limit them. It is about creating boundless possibilities, not conforming to any single vision. It is about ensuring that every person on the planet is free and able to explore whichever possibilities they choose. The only way to create a future of unlimited possibilities that are freely accessible to all is to use technology to build a world of overwhelming abundance.

Acceleration

We have seen throughout the previous chapters that we cannot hope to solve climate change and other serious environmental problems by chipping away at the edges, applying a band-aid here and there, and hoping that a bunch of small changes will add up to something useful. After 50 years of meager results, it is time to admit this strategy just does not work. We have also seen that simply doing less of what got us into trouble in the first place will not solve our problems: we cannot get out of the hole we have dug for ourselves by continuing to dig, only more slowly.

To build a brighter future, we need to fundamentally change the way we meet basic human needs, and that means changing how we get our energy, transportation, and food. It also means changing the way work itself gets done. Throughout the previous chapters we saw that the disruption of energy, transportation, food, and labor are poised to do precisely this over the next two decades, and as a result we are on the cusp of one of the most profound transformations in human history. Although these disruptions are inevitable, we must work hard to be prepared ahead of time so that we can take advantage of the extraordinary opportunities they present. We must also be vigilant to protect and support the individuals and communities who will be negatively impacted by the collapse of the incumbent fossil fuel, animal agriculture, seafood, and other disrupted industries along the way.

But then what?

Change won't stop when these four disruptions are complete. In the 2040s, technology will only be advancing faster. And in the 2050s, even faster. And in the 2060s, even faster still. There is no stable condition, no final destination, no station at the end of the line at which we will one day 'arrive' – at least not one we can begin to imagine.[98]

So then what do environmentalism and sustainability even mean within the context of accelerating change?

To answer this question, we must return to the foundations of environmental problems themselves.

Rethinking environmental problems

In Chapter 2, we saw that all contemporary environmental problems are framed by three underlying assumptions: *scarcity* (that natural resources are too few and dwindling), *degradation* (that human activity is always harmful and often irreversible), and *dependency* (that we will remain forever reliant upon ecosystem services to meet our needs).

What we saw in the subsequent chapters is that instead of using our existing tools to tinker at the margins within the confines of our current paradigm, a far better way to solve environmental problems is to flip the script on all three of these assumptions with entirely new and better tools. Clean technologies like solar power, electric vehicles, and cellular agriculture won't just let us reduce the ecological footprint of energy, transportation, and food by a few percent – they will let us slash the direct impacts of these cornerstone industries of the global economy while at the same time giving us the prosperity we need to undo prior damage of all kinds, and start actively healing the planet as well. And these technologies are just the beginning – the truly tectonic shifts will come from the automation of labor.

In a fundamental sense, it is scarcity, degradation, and dependency themselves that are our *real* environmental problems. Up until now, environmentalism has been virtually synonymous with learning to accept and live within the dictates of these three constraints. But that has made it an inherently dismal and defeatist enterprise, because as long as conditions of scarcity, degradation, and dependency persist, every victory for the environment will come at a terrible cost to humanity and vice versa. We have been trapped up until now in a no-win scenario, so it is no wonder the global environmental movement has been captured by misanthropy and doomsaying.

It does not have to continue like this. We can change the rules of the game. The best way to solve environmental problems is to end the conditions that create them in the first place, and that means overcoming scarcity, degradation, and dependency themselves.

From scarcity to abundance

Scarcity, as we saw in Chapter 3, is ultimately caused by a shortage of labor. Energy and transportation and food, along with all other goods and services, are only expensive because of all the labor required at every step in every supply chain to mine and refine and design and manufacture and assemble and transport and install everything they are comprised of – and that includes preventing and managing and cleaning up waste along the way. It follows that if we had an unlimited supply of ultra-cheap labor, very few things would be scarce enough to warrant having a price tag.

Up until now, however, we have been stuck in a self-limiting feedback loop with respect to labor and scarcity, because the more we increase the labor supply the old-fashioned way by growing our population, the more we must divide the fruits of our labor. The only way to really achieve escape velocity and free ourselves from the confines of scarcity is to decouple labor from human beings entirely, and that means with automation.

Unlike human labor, automation is massively scalable. We have already seen explosions in productivity from mechanization, where machines have replaced humans in the performance of simple, repetitive tasks. From textiles to farming to construction to calculation, machines have expanded our capacity to do useful work by many orders of magnitude. But mechanization via machines without any brains is still quite limited because those machines must either be piloted by a human being, or else be confined to a single function within a highly-controlled setting like a factory production line. Automation via intelligent machines is a different story altogether. Even with just narrow, algorithmic intelligence like the software in self-driving cars, robots will be adaptive enough to perform an enormous new range of tasks throughout the economy – they do not need to be sentient like C3PO or Commander Data. Nor do robots need to be anthropomorphic. Just like animals, they will come in all shapes and sizes, depending on what jobs they are made to do (although anthropomorphic robots are still likely to be both popular and useful for general purposes). Autonomous vehicles will likely be the breakout 'killer app', the pebble that starts the automation avalanche, and from there we should expect to see the same software 'brain' ported to other form factors – from humanoid bots and boxes-on-wheels to insect-like and fish-like bots, and everything in between.

Intelligence has always been the limiting factor for replacing human labor with machines. Once we break through that barrier, the sky is the limit. Unlike people, non-sentient robots don't take 20 years to reproduce and train, they don't need rest, and they don't need to be paid. None of the old rules about scarcity will apply, because the self-limiting feedback loop of population growth will no longer exist. Is energy scarce and expensive? Build more robots to make more energy. Are raw materials scarce and expensive? Build more robots to obtain more raw materials. Are natural resources scarce and expensive? Build more robots to cultivate more natural resources. If anything is scarce and expensive, including robots themselves, then the answer is just to build more robots – including robots to clean up any mess made along the way. (And don't forget: all of these robots will built by robots). If this seems a bit far-fetched, keep in mind that we have already been doing exactly this same thing throughout history with biological robots: us. The difference is that 'building' people is comparatively slow, and human population growth is severely self-limiting.

The disruption of labor will end most forms of scarcity as we know it, especially in combination with clean energy. Together, they will usher in an entirely new paradigm in which material abundance is the rule rather than the exception. Because all of our economics and most of our other social institutions are designed around scarcity, it is almost impossible to overstate how profound this paradigm shift will be. It will transform human life as completely as language, fire, the wheel, or electricity. This point deserves the strongest possible emphasis, so let me reiterate it here once more:

> *The system shock from the disruption of labor by AI, robotics, and automation will be staggering.*

Although the effects of the labor disruption will be overwhelmingly beneficial in the longer term, we need to be prepared well in advance to minimize the harms to individuals, communities, and society along the way.

A final point to emphasize here is that it doesn't really matter if the artificial intelligence and robotics technologies required for widespread automation arrive as soon as my research team expects. Whether the technology matures in the 2030s or the 2050s makes little real difference in the grand scheme of things. What matters is that it is only a few decades away, not centuries or millennia.

From degradation to healing

Environmental degradation, as we have discussed repeatedly in the preceding chapters, is an unintended consequence of imperfect tools whose use takes a large toll. Energy, transportation, and food are not inherently bad things themselves. To the contrary, they are wonderfully beneficial things that are only harmful because the technologies we have used to produce them in the past take a large toll on the natural environment.

Today, preventing ecological degradation and restoring degraded ecosystems is prohibitively expensive. But that will change as the disruption of energy, transportation, food, and labor slashes the cost of mitigation and restoration across the board. These disruptions will also give us the overall prosperity we need to meet environmental challenges that have so far been too large or too diffuse to deal with. The most obvious example is climate change. With today's technology, the task of reaching net zero emissions alone seems daunting, and to go beyond that and remove hundreds of gigatons of carbon from the atmosphere and oceans seems all but impossible. But by the 2040s, the combination of clean energy, clean transportation, billions of acres of land freed from animal agriculture, and a superabundance of automated labor will make both of these tasks feasible, offering a truly complete solution to the climate crisis.

Other examples of environmental problems like marine plastic pollution and soil contamination follow the same logic, especially if we look a little further into the future and consider the possibilities offered by extremely large numbers of intelligent machines. To frame the picture here, consider that every scrap of litter, every shred of waste, every drop of toxic gunk or goop you and I have ever seen *could* have been cleaned up, if someone – or some*thing* – had had the time and energy and inclination to do so. We saw in Chapter 3 that biology itself provides the existence proof that very small machines can still be immensely complicated. Biology also proves that with enough of these machines, it is possible to make large-scale transformations of the physical world with molecular precision. By the second half of this century, our robotics and computing technology will have advanced to the point where we can cheaply produce huge numbers of machines the size of insects (microbots) and even microbes (nanobots) that can run reasonably sophisticated software. These devices could then be set to the task of cleaning up waste in the same way that ants will happily clean up every last crumb of food you spill in the grass at a picnic. And just as biological organisms of various sizes process biodegradable waste across entire landscapes with molecular precision, so too might slightly-brainy nonbiological machines process nonbiodegradable pollution at a similar scale and precision.

Ecological restoration takes more than just cleanup, of course – especially on land. Returning a landscape to a prior state of biodiversity and complex functioning involves carefully reintroducing and cultivating native species over time, relentlessly removing invasive species, managing fire and water to promote appropriate patterns of disturbance and succession and soil structure, preventing inbreeding by ensuring sufficient genetic diversity, reconsolidating fragmented habitat, and other forms of judicious human intervention. This is expensive and demanding work. Here too, however, the direct benefits that the disruptions and their technologies will bring to the challenge is self-evident – as is the overall prosperity they will usher in.

Taken together, the four disruptions will render both mitigating ongoing ecological degradation and restoring ecosystem integrity affordable at a planetary scale. They will allow us to shift from a paradigm of harm to one of healing, and let us rebuild our damaged biosphere to an extent environmentalists have never dared to dream was possible before.

Once again, it is important to stress that it makes little difference in the greater arc of history whether this technology arrives by the 2030s or the 2050s. The point is that it lies only a few decades ahead, not centuries or millennia away.

From dependence to freedom

Today, we care about the environment primarily because we are dependent upon it. Ecosystem services provide our air, water, food, fiber, and much else that we cannot live without. But this utilitarian stance, which forms the basis of the *conservation ethic*, views the rest of the living world merely as a tool for our benefit – a reservoir of instrumental value whose only worth is its usefulness. As such, it is obviously a very anthropocentric position, albeit an effective one from a policymaking and advocacy standpoint. Indeed, the most reliable way to safeguard the fate of our forests and wetlands and coral reefs up until now has been to make the case that *our* wellbeing depends on *their* wellbeing. But this is a dangerous game to play, for two important reasons.

The first reason is that dependence of this kind, as in other aspects of our lives, is not healthy. Dependency is precarious, constraining, and inherently creates a conflict of interest that can lead to resentment. We have already seen a strong political divide emerge in many societies around environmental issues because people disagree about how much exploitation of nature is acceptable. As long as a tradeoff relationship exists between humanity and the natural world based on dependency, there will always be disagreement over where to strike the balance – and this has led to conflict and violence many times in many places throughout history.[99,100]

The second reason is that arguments for sustainability based on dependence will only weaken over time as technology grants us ever-greater control over the physical world. This would make no difference if the time horizon for environmental problems were just a few months, but environmental issues are inherently long-term concerns stretching out decades or centuries ahead, and on that timescale betting the farm on a horse that is slowing down is not a winning strategy.

Dependency is not a good thing, and hanging our hopes for the future of the environment on it is both toxic and shortsighted. Nature will always remain a target for exploitation as long as we are reliant upon it, and so the logical implication here is clear: the best way to avoid *overexploiting* nature is to *never need to exploit it at all.* That means we must shift from dependence to freedom, both for our sake and for the sake of the planet. The only conceivable way to do so is through technological progress.

Although the four disruptions we have discussed represent a major step in the direction of decoupling human material prosperity from environmental impacts, it will be quite a while before we can meet all material needs without any ecological footprint at all. Nevertheless, that science fiction level of technology will inevitably become a reality, and whether it is 2060 or 2080 or 2100 makes no fundamental difference. The point, yet again, is that it will only be a matter of decades rather than centuries or millennia.

From science fiction to science fact

Everything is impossible until it isn't.

On the one hand, we have seen that the technologies driving the disruption of energy, transportation, food, and labor are science fact, not science fiction. Solar, wind, and batteries are already here. Electric and autonomous vehicles are already here. Precision fermentation and cellular agriculture are already here. Narrow artificial intelligence and robotics are already here. With each of these technologies, we have left the breakthrough R&D phase and are now in the refinement and deployment phase.

On the other hand, many technologies that will unquestionably be instrumental in solving environmental problems later this century truly are still just science fiction today, which is why my research team does not include them in our formal analyses. It's also why I haven't brought them into in any of this book's previous discussions until now. But as we approach the end of our journey, let's indulge in speculation for just a few moments and consider some of the more exotic technological advancements that we can confidently expect to emerge between now and the year 2100.

To start, we have challenged the assumption that scarcity, degradation, and dependence are forever inescapable. We have seen that it is quite straightforward to imagine a future in which clean energy and automated labor are so superabundant that humanity could – if it chose to – mitigate all ongoing environmental impacts and restore all past ecological damage. And, for better or worse, the prospect of being able to solve all of today's environmental problems in the not-too-terribly-distant future obviously casts these concerns in a new light. But does figuring out how to solve today's environmental problems really go far enough? Are there other fundamental assumptions about humanity's relationship with nature besides scarcity, degradation, and dependence that technological progress will lead us to question?

Indeed there are, and to find them we can turn to an unlikely example for illustration: cheeseburgers.

We have already seen that as a first step, the four disruptions will allow us to produce a superabundance of nearly costless cheeseburgers by assigning all of today's making-cheeseburgers-from-cows tasks to robots powered by clean energy. And this would be a significant improvement over the status quo on many levels. But we can do better. We have also already seen that as a second step, instead of using robots to raise and slaughter cows, we could instead make meat and dairy products of much higher quality and variety without any animal agriculture whatsoever using precision fermentation and cellular agriculture technologies. This would allow us to meet the demand for cheeseburgers without such a massive ecological footprint or horrific animal suffering – so far, so good. But we can do even better still. What if, as a third step, we were to go further and produce all of those precision fermentation and cellular agriculture cheeseburgers outside of the Earth's biosphere entirely? What if all our production facilities were deep underground? Or even in outer space? That way, cheeseburgers would genuinely have no ecological footprint at all! We cannot do any better than outer space, can we? As a matter of fact, we can: what if instead of simply finding better ways to meet our *existing* demand for cheeseburgers, we take a final step and use technology to remove our *desire* for cheeseburgers altogether?

Virtually all of our human needs – physical, social, psychological – are ultimately rooted in our inherited *Homo sapiens* biology. Cheeseburgers taste good to us because they contain things that our distant ancestors evolved to crave: fat, protein, starch, and salt. The range of human preferences, whether for food or housing or entertainment or anything else, is quite narrowly circumscribed by our genes. There is individual variation of course; some people prefer sushi to cheeseburgers, and vice versa. But no normal human being prefers the taste of asphalt or uranium ore to sushi or cheeseburgers. Our personal preferences are subject only to very modest adjustment via education, enculturation, and self-discipline. But technology could radically alter this situation. Might we eat more carrots and fewer cheeseburgers if we could modify our brains to make carrots *taste like* cheeseburgers? (And make cheeseburgers taste like… well, you can fill in the blank here with your imagination).

The practical implications of opening our preferences to redesign are mind-boggling, to say nothing of the philosophical implications. But these are not the only fundamental changes we will make to ourselves through biotechnology.

We are also likely to end aging in the decades ahead, so that before the year 2100 there will be no more 'old' people – only people who were born a long time ago. Might we care more about the future of the environment if we all knew we were still going to be around to see it? Alternatively, if we all stopped aging and dying, wouldn't overpopulation and stagnation become more serious concerns? (Maybe so, but these are comparatively good problems to have, and certainly far better ones to leave our children and grandchildren with than the horrors of aging-related suffering and 60 million deaths each year).

After being stigmatized for generations, anti-aging and regenerative medicine technology has at last become mainstream science in the last decade and is now progressing at a breakneck pace, with billions of dollars in funding pouring in each year. Researchers are just starting to have real success in mice, not just in slowing down aging, but in actually turning back the clock in middle age and rejuvenating them as well.[101,102]

Likewise, virtually all disease and disability are likely to be eradicated before the year 2100 as well, whether via treatments that are familiar today such as drugs and vaccines and gene therapies, or via more advanced technologies that still lie decades away such as nanobots that fight infection and repair injuries, replacement organs and limbs grown in the lab, and cybernetic implants that restore or enhance our physical and mental functioning. Might we be more optimistic in general if our youth and vitality were perpetual instead of precarious and fleeting? Or, more darkly, might we care *less* about issues like air pollution and soil contamination if we were invulnerable to the illnesses they cause today?

What about the rest of the natural world? The same advanced technologies that give us greater control over our own bodies will allow us to accomplish wonders for other living things as well. We are already nearing the point where we can resurrect recently-extinct species such as wooly mammoths, and the science of de-extinction is a rapidly advancing field.[103–105] More ancient species may also be recoverable, or at least facsimiles of them recreated, in the style of Jurassic Park. Although we must of course be cautious and thoughtful not to abuse such technology, as the movie so entertainingly warns, it is nevertheless clearly prudent to preserve tissue samples of endangered species today for de-extinction efforts in the future

– and indeed, a number of organizations such as the San Diego Zoo and The Frozen Ark are doing conservation genomics and DNA banking work of just this sort.[106],[107] Moreover, if we go beyond individual endangered species, we can think of entire ecosystems facing degradation as being endangered as well. With the same de-extinction technology applied alongside restoration ecology, we will be able to restore entire lost ecosystems – but only if we have a comprehensive knowledge of their biodiversity to build upon, which means we need to exhaustively document their structure and composition today while we still have the chance.

But once we do have de-extinction technologies in our hands, do we have an obligation to bring back *all* extinct species and ecosystems? If not, how do we decide which ones deserve resurrection? Should we bring back only those that we have extinguished in the last 100 years? Or 1,000 years? Or 10,000 years? Should we return landscapes to the way they were just a few generations ago? Or should we turn the clock back to the end of the last ice age?

Lastly, no playful speculation about the future of technology can be complete without mentioning *artificial general intelligence*, or AGI. With some notable exceptions like Ray Kurzweil, most computer science experts used to believe that sentient, self-aware AGI would not arrive until the second half of the 21st Century. But breakthroughs over the last decade in deep learning technologies have shifted the consensus forward, so that the majority of experts surveyed now believe there is a good chance AGI could emerge in the 2030s.

Regardless of the exact timeline, when AGI emerges we have reason to expect that its inherent ability to inspect and refine the architecture of its own mind will result in a recursive feedback loop of self-improvement that the mathematician I.J. Good in 1965 called an 'intelligence explosion'. Any AGI is thus likely to become *superintelligent* very rapidly. Because we have no way of predicting the actions of any entity that is substantially more intelligent than ourselves, all we can say is that soon after AGI arises, it is possible we could see the pace of technological advancement accelerate to a previously unimaginable rate. Whether this would be a good thing or a bad thing will depend on whether the superintelligent AGI is friendly towards humanity and other living things or not. In the event that AGI is hostile, there is probably not much we can do about it, just as there is not much that chimpanzees or chickens can do about the hostilities of human beings. But in the event that AGI is friendly, this would be exceedingly good news both for us and for the environment. So, as Stephen Hawking said, AGI will either be the best or the worst thing that ever happens to us. Fingers crossed.

To be sure, this is all still the stuff of science fiction, and we won't go any further down the rabbit hole here. The full environmental implications of radical technological advancements – fascinating as they may be – are a topic for another book. But these technologies will not remain science fiction much longer. For our purposes here, it is enough just to recognize that if we wish to think seriously about long-term environmental change, then we must also be willing to think seriously about long-term technological change as well. The lengthy time horizon of environmental concerns means that we environmentalists have an obligation to also be futurists, because even if we ourselves don't live to see these technologies become a reality, our children certainly will – just as they will certainly live to feel the worst impacts of climate change if we refuse to do anything about it. We owe it to our children and the planet to take both the environment and technology seriously, if we wish to safeguard their shared future.

Rethinking environmentalism and sustainability in the 21ˢᵗ Century

What if we actually succeed?

What if there does indeed come a time when we no longer have *any* environmental problems caused by scarcity, degradation, or dependence – and not centuries or millennia from now, but just a few decades hence? What then?

We will need to rethink what it means to care about the environment in the 21ˢᵗ Century.

The overwhelming majority of contemporary environmental policymaking, planning, and activism is centered upon the conservation ethic which values nature because it is useful to us. This has been a perfectly pragmatic approach to environmentalism so far, but it won't work forever. Defining your personal or organizational identity too narrowly around a problem can be a risky prospect in any domain, because solving that problem would mean destroying your identity. For the last 50 years, since the birth of the modern environmental movement, it has been reasonable to dismiss the moral hazard of misaligned incentives here because real solutions to our environmental problems have never really seemed within reach, and anyway there have always been other problems to pivot to. But over the next 50 years we will solve virtually all of our environmental problems, one after the next, and along the way the purely instrumental value of nature will erode to almost nothing as technological advancement inexorably marches onward. Decoupling from nature is not a matter of *if*, only a matter of *when*. Fighting for a cause is all to the good, but if we truly plan to *win* the fight for the environment – and I certainly do – then we need a plan for what comes afterward as well.

To some extent, every crusade and movement, every project great or small, faces this same conundrum of how to move on with grace after victory. In the case of environmentalism, we will need to shift over the course of this century to a *preservation ethic* of valuing nature not for our sake but for its own sake instead. One powerful way to think about this transformation is as a developmental arc in humanity's relationship with the natural world.

Figure 23: Developmental arc of the human-nature relationship.

When our journey as a species began hundreds of thousands of years ago, in Stage 1, we were hunter-gatherers who were little different than any another animal on the landscape. We took what resources and services we could from the natural world, but our ecological footprint was so small that there was little need to give back.

We entered Stage 2 with the advent of settled agriculture, and since then we have become increasingly proficient at exploiting nature for its resources and services. For most of recorded history, our general relationship with nature has been similar to that of farmers and miners whose focus is maximizing extraction from the landscape irrespective of the ecology that was there before.

In just the past few decades, however, we have finally started to get serious about giving back to nature, and so we are beginning to enter Stage 3. Like gardeners and foresters, we are still focused on exploiting nature for its resources and services, but we now realize that sustaining resource extraction over the long-run requires a mindset of care and cultivation. We have also shifted from our previous condition of pure dependence to a novel condition of co-dependence with nature. In other words, we still depend upon nature, but nature also now depends upon our largesse for its own survival and wellbeing as well.

Conventional environmentalism holds that we needn't go any further than Stage 3. But I have argued throughout this book that merely graduating from reckless exploiters into 'sustainable' exploiters of nature is not good enough. I believe we must go further.

In Stage 4 we will begin to move away from exploitation entirely. Instead, we will assume the role of ecologists with a focus on restoring and rewilding large swathes of the planet's landscapes and oceans. I believe we can and must do far better than just 'living within our means'. We must set our sights far higher than the meager aspirations of 'degrowth', and commit to giving back to nature *vastly* more than we take – healing old wounds and righting past wrongs wherever possible. As we have seen, however, the only way to take that next step on our journey is with the aid of technology.

Our journey *could* stop there. Indeed, many of us already do cherish nature for its beauty, for its connections to our heritage and culture, and as a source of knowledge and inspiration. And although these are still anthropocentric in the sense that they are benefits nature confers to *us*, they are nevertheless benefits that are maximized not by exploiting but rather by nurturing the rest of the living world. Stage 4 is thus where we genuinely shift from the zero-sum win-lose relationship between humanity and nature of the past to the nonzero win-win relationship of the future.

However, I think that we should aspire to go even further. I personally believe our ultimate responsibility and environmental destiny is to become stewards and guardians of this priceless blue gem we call Earth, tumbling through the otherwise dark and desolate cosmos. I am hopeful that one day, perhaps by the end of this century, we will progress to Stage 5 and seek our future among the stars. When that day comes, our ancestral homeworld will cease to be a place we occupy, but instead will become a museum we explore with reverence, a park we visit with care, and a wilderness we cherish and protect.

We have a long journey ahead of us. So, what steps do we need to take in order to get from here to there?

Here are some key organizing principles upon which to build a new environmentalism for the 21st Century:

1. Embrace technological progress as central to environmentalism.

We cannot ignore technological progress, because it will be a major driving force for change in our world on the same time scale as environmental concerns themselves. Nor should we wish for no technological progress to occur, because the expansion of practical knowledge that new technologies embody offers our best hope for creating a brighter future, both for humanity and for the rest of the natural world.

As a general rule, one of the best things we can all do for the environment is to adopt new clean technology as early as possible, whether as individuals or industries or entire societies. Early adoption acts as a crucial accelerant for technological progress, providing demand and alleviating risk for pioneering innovators when they need it most.

2. Adopt a practical, problem-solving mindset.

Environmental issues are not an epic struggle to be romanticized, or an inescapable feature of the human condition, or divine retribution for our hubris. They are not sins we must atone for, or the unavoidable consequences of enjoying a modern quality of life. They are not retribution or karma or justice. They are just problems. And problems are solvable with the right knowledge.

If the fight for the environment is a fight we actually want to win, then it is essential we frame our concerns as problems so that we can figure out exactly what knowledge – meaning what science and technology and policies and institutions – we need to solve them.

3. Forge alliances around solutions.

Environmental issues ought to be viewed as universal apolitical concerns shared by everyone. The value of clean air, biodiversity, and climate stability can and should be as uncontroversial as the value of nutrition, healthcare, and literacy. Instead, environmentalism has been captured by ideology and divided along standard tribal lines: conservative versus liberal, rich versus poor, 'Global North' versus 'Global South'. Allowing environmental issues to become politicized was a massive strategic error and moral failure, and therefore one of the greatest mistakes of modern environmentalism. It has severely undermined everything we are trying to accomplish.

Moving forward, the new environmentalism of the 21st Century must reunite us around shared values and goals, and perhaps the best way to do this is with a pragmatic approach that focuses on solutions. For example, the energy disruption driven by solar, wind, and batteries is a win for almost everyone: it's a win for climate change, a win for clean air, a win for new jobs, a win for energy independence, a win for both rich and poor, a win for almost every nation, and a win for social and economic prosperity across the board. Solutions give everyone something to like, whatever their other differences may be, and we must leverage that shared interest as an opportunity to stop fighting one another and start working together.

4. Target environmental problems at their source.

It is better to cure a disease than to treat its symptoms. If you have a cracked tooth and it is decaying, the solution is not to mask the problem with mouthwash or desensitizing toothpaste. Nor is the solution to stop chewing and hope the damage resolves on its own. The solution is to *fix your tooth*. Similarly, if the problem is that electricity generation emits greenhouse gases, the solution is not a patchwork of band-aid treatments like smokestack scrubbers, 'clean' coal, or high-efficiency gas turbines. Nor is the solution to stop using energy. The solution is to *generate electricity without emitting greenhouse gases*. If the problem is that combustion engine vehicles cause air pollution, the solution is not catalytic converters, fuel additives, or smaller cars. Nor is the solution to stop traveling. The solution is *vehicles without combustion engines*. If the problem is that animal products carry an enormous ecological footprint, the solution is not to recycle chicken manure, zap cattle effluent slurry with artificial lightning, or use fish bycatch and waste as aquaculture feed.[108,109] Nor is the solution to stop eating meat and eggs and dairy. The solution is *animal products made without animals*.

Even more fundamentally, we have seen that virtually all environmental problems ultimately arise as a consequence of scarcity, degradation, or dependence, and so the real solution is to create conditions of abundance, restoration, and freedom that obviate these underlying problems entirely.

5. Prioritize which environmental problems to solve first based not just on their immediate harmfulness, but also on their irreversibility.

When your house is on fire, you not only have to decide how best to extinguish the flames, but also which of your belongings are most important to save. When people face this tragic choice in real life, they invariably prioritize objects that are irreplaceable – old photographs, childhood keepsakes, family heirlooms (and of course their pets, although these are obviously not possessions in the way that inanimate objects are). Nobody braves the flames to rescue a pair of socks than can easily be replaced.

The same logic applies to saving the environment. Not all ecological damage is permanent, and we should prioritize our efforts such that we are sure to prevent truly irreversible impacts. It is only rational that we ought to prioritize saving culturally sacred groves of 3,000-year-old giant sequoia trees over picking up trash on the street, because one form of impact is irreversible and the other is not. The challenge here, however, is that some impacts which are difficult to reverse today will become reversible in the future with new technology, while others will not, and we need to know which is which.

Plastic litter, for example, is already a reversible impact today, and will become even more readily reversible in the future thanks to abundant clean energy and automated labor. Endangered species are irreversible today, but will become reversible in the future as long as we are sure to collect the necessary tissue samples beforehand. But no technology can fully repair the loss of a sacred grove of 3,000-year-old giant sequoia trees, because even if the trees could be perfectly duplicated they would still only be duplicates and not the authentic originals. (Indeed, as duplication of all material things becomes progressively easier, it is likely that authenticity will become a paramount source of value in the future, just like it is with famous paintings today).

This is almost certain to be a contentious source of debate, because forms of mitigation that seem very important today will need to slip in the order of priority once we recognize the reversibility implications of future technologies. Freshwater supplies, for example, seem scarce and vital to conserve today, but a superabundance of clean energy and automated labor will make desalination and long-distance water distribution dirt cheap. So while conserving freshwater and protecting sacred giant sequoia groves might seem equally important at the present moment, such equivocation of priorities is badly misguided in light of technological progress.

6.   Reframe our relationship with nature from zero-sum (win-lose) to nonzero (win-win).

New clean technologies can meet human needs while simultaneously reducing, eliminating, and even repairing our ecological impacts. In doing so, these technologies will change the game by realigning our interests and incentives, making human prosperity and ecological integrity mutually reinforcing rather than mutually exclusive. We must stop fixating on the conflict between humanity and nature – or worse yet, romanticizing it – and instead make a mission of seeking out and seizing opportunities for win-wins.

7.   Think beyond just mitigation and plan for restoration as well.

If your house is on fire, putting out the flames is only the first step in solving the problem. Repairing the damage afterwards is just as important, and often the harder part – as we saw with climate change. This same logic applies to virtually all environmental issues. Even for problems like deforestation, from which the Earth could recover on its own given enough time, new technologies will enable us to greatly accelerate the natural recovery process.

Our current mindset of mitigation and sustainable exploitation does not go far enough to realize environmental values and goals. We need a restoration and revitalization mindset that lets us think like ecologists and healers instead.

8. Recognize that change is coming, and get ready for it.

Radical technological change is inevitable. We cannot stop it. We cannot ignore it. And we must not obstruct it. It is no good burying our heads in the sand and pretending the world will be the same tomorrow as it is today. The pace of technological progress will only accelerate for the foreseeable future, and the more we environmentalists resist or dismiss it, the more our voice and legitimacy will erode. If we keep claiming that technology cannot solve environmental problems while solar power and electric vehicles and precision fermentation are all growing exponentially, the world will simply stop taking us seriously.

Whether from missed opportunities such as Puerto Rico's failure to rebuild its shattered energy system with renewables after the disaster of Hurricane Maria in 2017, or from shortsighted vulnerabilities such as Europe's continued reliance on Russian oil and gas leading up to the invasion of Ukraine in 2022, the global environmental movement has either stood idly by or actively hampered societies' efforts to embrace new, clean technology as soon as possible.[110] We cannot continue making this mistake, especially now that the disruption of energy, transportation, food, and labor are imminent.

As a general strategy, anticipating change ahead of time and being well-prepared to take advantage of the opportunities it presents is a crucial means of maximizing wellbeing and avoiding harm in any domain – and this is just as true for entire societies as it is in our own personal lives. Why should it be any different for change of the technological kind? Or for opportunities in the environmental domain?

9. Celebrate progress and take the wins.

Failure to adequately acknowledge progress and claim past environmental victories has been a major strategic error of the modern environmental movement. Although the sense of urgency around environmental issues is of course justified, the public and policymakers have become fatigued and jaded by what is widely perceived to be a near-total lack of environmental progress. Indeed, many people are under the impression that things have only ever gotten worse – and this is patently false.

Safe drinking water, sanitation, indoor air quality, air pollution, acid rain, CFCs, bans on whaling, the recovery of certain endangered species such as bald eagles, and the expansion of forest coverage in North America and Europe are all examples of environmental progress we have made worldwide since the advent of modern environmentalism. But, if anything, we environmentalists have downplayed these successes rather than highlighted them. That has been a serious blunder.

Instead, it is crucial that we celebrate the progress we have made, and take the wins we have fought so hard to achieve. Highlighting our successes going forward will help us retain the interest and support of the public and policymakers, as well as build the momentum we need to tackle major challenges like climate change.

10. Distinguish intended from unintended consequences.

Today, many of us in the environmental community demonize consumption – especially of energy, transportation, and food – as if they were harmful in and of themselves. Partly this is because their harmful side effects have seemed inherent and unavoidable up to now, and partly this is because consumption itself can be moralized in purely psychological terms as selfish, indulgent, gluttonous, and so forth. But this is a mistake.

Energy isn't bad, energy is *good* – greenhouse gas emissions are bad. Transportation isn't bad, transportation is *good* – traffic and air pollution are bad. Food isn't bad, food is *good* – deforestation and animal suffering are bad. As it stands, too many of us falsely conflate the good with the bad as if they can never be decoupled, and this has led to the misguided conclusion that consuming *less* energy, transportation, and food is somehow more socially desirable or environmentally sustainable than switching to *clean* energy, transportation, and food. We have seen why this thinking is dead wrong with the burning house analogy again and again throughout this book.

If we are to build a new and more meaningful environmentalism for the 21st Century, we must stop throwing the baby out with the bathwater and clearly distinguish intended consequences from unintended ones from now on.

11. Recognize both individual and collective responsibility for environmental problems.

Environmental problems have causes at multiple levels of analysis. Yes, consumer demand drives the production of goods and services with harmful environmental side effects, and so our individual choices matter. And yes, a relatively small number of multinational corporations and government agencies are responsible for the majority of that production, so regulation of industry matters.

But it is unproductive to try to assign more blame one way or the other. In particular, both the modern environmental movement and polluting industries have both tried to lay the majority of responsibility at the feet of individuals – for different reasons. Environmentalists have wanted to activate people and give them tangible actions to take, whereas industries have more cynically aimed to divert attention away from the need for regulation by blaming consumers for their profligate lifestyle choices. But rather than shifting blame *from* individuals *to* industries, as is the current trend, we should stop playing the blame game altogether. As the saying goes, *everyone sucks here.*

Instead, we must recognize that both individual and collective responsibility for environmental problems exist and are deeply intertwined, and take a pragmatic approach to solving these problems by identifying which concrete measures can be taken at each level.

12. Emphasize the intrinsic value of nature.

Although modern environmentalism is built overwhelmingly upon the instrumental value of the natural world, meaning its usefulness to us, nature nevertheless has its own intrinsic value and right to exist independent of us as well. This topic has been thoroughly explored by scientists, scholars, and philosophers – particularly as part of the *deep ecology* school of thought.[78,111–115] Going forward, we will need to progressively integrate more and more of this thinking into 21st

Century environmentalism as humanity's dependence upon nature diminishes. This will be particularly important as we move beyond the present paradigm of sustainable exploitation into a new paradigm of restoration, and then eventually (I believe) into a paradigm in which our ultimate role is as stewards and guardians of nature.

13. Be passionate about the brighter future we are fighting *for*, not just about the darker future we are fighting *against*.

The environmentalism of the 21st Century must be built on optimism, not pessimism.

If we want our friends and family to care about the environment and take action, if we want the public and policymakers to heed our warnings and support our cause, then we must communicate a clear vision of the brighter future we are fighting for. Fear-mongering and guilt-tripping might have had their uses in the past, but they will take us no further. Negativity has never been inspiring, and the world has had enough of our whining, complaining, and naysaying. People need more than just fear and guilt. They need compelling, well-evidenced reasons to hope too, and so far we environmentalists have utterly failed them.

Doomsaying, cynicism, and other forms of self-indulgent pessimism are craven and childish. It is time to grow up. We must dare to envision a brighter future, and then dare to be optimistic as we do the hard work of striving to achieve it.[116]

Moving forward

As we have seen repeatedly in the previous chapters, regress won't work. Nevertheless, the idea of degrowth and austerity has always been popular because it appeals to our natural instinct to freeze and retreat from danger. But there are times when that is exactly the wrong move, and unfortunately this is one of them. Climate change and other major environmental problems are not like a sleeping bear we have stumbled upon in the woods. We cannot solve them by slowly and carefully backtracking the way we came. Instead, the more accurate analogy we have used through this book is that of a house on fire, so let's return to it one last time.

Your house is on fire. What should you do?

Put the fire out. Not some of it, *all* of it. Not slowly over the next 50 years, *now*. Not with the bucket you have immediately at hand, but by calling the Fire Department to bring the real tools for the job.

Save what matters most. Not things that can be replaced today, or tomorrow, or next year, but things that can *never* be replaced.

Fix the damage. Rebuild what was broken and restore what was lost. Don't wait for things to fix themselves.

Install smoke alarms. Take action to safeguard the entire building so a disaster like this can never happen again.

Conventional environmentalism misses the mark every step of the way, so it's time to rethink our approach from the ground up. We cannot go backward. A stumbling, uninspired retreat from the challenges of the present will not magically return us to the halcyon days of old. There is no childhood innocence to which we can return, no nest from which we can unfledge, no cave in which we can huddle to wait out the storm. We have grievously wounded our world, and now we must rise to the challenge of healing it.

As with so many other challenges in life and history, the only way we can succeed is by moving forward.

A brighter future

We are on the cusp of a phase change for human civilization. It would be extraordinary enough if even one foundational sector of the global economy were poised for disruption, but we are going to see energy, transportation, food, and labor all disrupted *simultaneously* over the next two decades. It is almost impossible to overstate the significance of the transformation that lies ahead.

We saw in Chapter 4 how the clean technologies driving these disruptions will enable us to rapidly shift away from using fossil fuels, combustion engines, and animal agriculture, while at the same time making it affordable to restore the climate system to a safe state by withdrawing hundreds of billions of tons of carbon from the atmosphere and oceans. That is cause for *real* optimism.

But that is just the beginning. We saw in Chapters 5, 6, and 7 how superabundant clean energy and labor will allow us to solve virtually all of today's environmental problems. Deforestation, desertification, habitat fragmentation and loss, overfishing, coral bleaching, eutrophication and hypoxic dead zones, ocean acidification, plastic pollution, biodiversity loss, endangered species, invasive species, air pollution, water pollution, soil erosion, soil contamination, and waste management – they will *all* become solvable over the next several decades thanks to the same technologies that are driving the disruptions today. That is cause for *real* optimism.

Even better still, the good news goes beyond just environmental challenges. These very same technologies will also help us achieve our social goals as well, because they are massively democratizing and will smash existing geographic and socioeconomic barriers to human development. With clean superabundance, we can have prosperity for everyone, everywhere, without ecological harm. Humanity can thrive, and we can heal our planet at the same time. That is cause for *real* optimism.

We stand at one of the most exciting moments in human history, brimming over with promise and possibility. There has never been greater reason to celebrate the prospect of progress. We have the tools we need to build a brighter future – for ourselves, for our children, for our planet.

Let's start building that future today, and let's build it together.

REFERENCES

1. Marks, E. *et al.* Young People's Voices on Climate Anxiety, Government Betrayal and Moral Injury: A Global Phenomenon. SSRN Scholarly Paper at https://doi.org/10.2139/ssrn.3918955 (2021).

2. Arbib, J., Seba, T. & Dorr, A. *Rethinking Climate Change 2020-2030*. https://www.rethinkx.com/climate-implications (2021).

3. Progress | Munk Debates. https://munkdebates.com/debates/progress.

4. Hickel, J., Klu, K. & Read, R. *Less Is More: How Degrowth Will Save the World*. (Windmill Books, 2021).

5. *Degrowth: A Vocabulary for a New Era*. (Routledge, 2014).

6. Kallis, G. *In defense of degrowth: Opinions and minifestos*. (Uneven Earth Press, 2018).

7. Brynjolfsson, E. & McAfee, A. *The Second Machine Age: Work, Progress, and Prosperity in a Time of Brilliant Technologies*. (W. W. Norton & Company, 2014).

8. The Breakthrough Institute. *The Ecomodernist Manifesto*. http://www.ecomodernism.org/manifesto/ (2015).

9. McAfee, A. *More from Less: The Surprising Story of How We Learned to Prosper Using Fewer Resources—and What Happens Next*. (Scribner, 2019).

10. Horowitz, J. Degrowth: A dangerous idea or the answer to the world's biggest crisis? | CNN Business. *CNN* https://www.cnn.com/2022/11/13/economy/degrowth-climate-cop27/index.html (2022).

11. Cowen, T. *Stubborn Attachments: A Vision for a Society of Free, Prosperous, and Responsible Individuals.* (Stripe Press, 2018).

12. Our World in Data. Where does the plastic in our oceans come from? *Our World in Data* https://ourworldindata.org/ocean-plastics (2021).

13. Box, J. E. *et al.* Greenland ice sheet climate disequilibrium and committed sea-level rise. *Nat. Clim. Change* 1–6 (2022) doi:10.1038/s41558-022-01441-2.

14. Foundation For Climate Restoration. Foundation for Climate Restoration. *Foundation For Climate Restoration* https://foundationforclimaterestoration.org/start-here/ (2022).

15. Lempert, R. J., Marangoni, G., Keller, K. & Duke, J. *Is Climate Restoration an Appropriate Climate Policy Goal?* https://www.rand.org/pubs/research_reports/RR2442.html (2018).

16. Huesemann, M. & Huesemann, J. *Techno-Fix: Why Technology Won't Save Us Or the Environment.* (New Society Publishers, 2011).

17. Lee, J. 8. When Horses Posed a Public Health Hazard. *City Room* https://cityroom.blogs.nytimes.com/2008/06/09/when-horses-posed-a-public-health-hazard/ (2008).

18. World Health Organization. WHO | Waterborne disease related to unsafe water and sanitation. *WHO* http://www.who.int/sustainable-development/housing/health-risks/waterborne-disease/en/ (2019).

19. World Health Organization. WHO | Household air pollution from cooking, heating and lighting. *WHO* http://www.who.int/sustainable-

development/housing/health-risks/household-air-pollution/en/ (2019).

20. Pinker, S. *Enlightenment Now: The Case for Reason, Science, Humanism, and Progress.* (Penguin, 2019).

21. Rosling, H., Rönnlund, A. R. & Rosling, O. *Factfulness: Ten Reasons We're Wrong About the World--and Why Things Are Better Than You Think.* (Flatiron Books, 2018).

22. Roser, M. The world is awful. The world is much better. The world can be much better. *Our World in Data* https://ourworldindata.org/much-better-awful-can-be-better (2022).

23. Coates, P. A. *Nature: western attitudes since ancient times.* (University of California Press, 2005).

24. Whatever Happened to Acid Rain? *Science History Institute* https://www.sciencehistory.org/distillations/podcast/whatever-happened-to-acid-rain (2018).

25. Adler, J. H. Fables of the Cuyahoga: Reconstructing a History of Environmental Protection. *Fordham Environ. Law J.* 14, 89–146 (2003).

26. Santas, A. Aristotelian Ethics and Biophilia. *Ethics Environ.* 19, 95–121 (2014).

27. Ehrlich, P. R. & Holdren, J. P. Critique. *Bull. At. Sci.* 28, 16–27 (1972).

28. Ehrlich, P. R. & Holdren, J. P. Impact of Population Growth. *Science* 171, 1212–1217 (1971).

29. UN DESA Population Division. World Population Prospects - Population Division - United Nations. *World Population Prospects 2017* https://population.un.org/wpp/ (2019).

30. IMF. *World Economic Outlook Update*.
    https://www.imf.org/en/Publications/WEO/Issues/2021/0
    1/26/2021-world-economic-outlook-update (2021).

31. ILO. *ILO Monitor: COVID-19 and the world of work (Sixth edition
    - updated estimates and analysis)*.
    https://www.ilo.org/wcmsp5/groups/public/---dgreports/---
    dcomm/documents/briefingnote/wcms_755910.pdf (2020).

32. The Ocean Cleanup. The Ocean Cleanup. *The Ocean Cleanup*
    https://theoceancleanup.com/ (2019).

33. Bostrom, N. *Superintelligence: Paths, Dangers, Strategies*. (Oxford
    University Press, 2014).

34. Bostrom, N. & Müller, V. C. Future Progress in Artificial
    Intelligence: A Survey of Expert Opinion. in *Computing and
    Philosophy* (ed. Müller, V. C.) vol. 375 (Springer: Synthese
    Library, 2016).

35. Toyama, K. *Geek Heresy: Rescuing Social Change from the Cult of
    Technology*. (PublicAffairs, 2015).

36. Camera & Imaging Products Association. *Digital Cameras
    Statistical Data*. http://www.cipa.jp/stats/dc_e.html (2019).

37. Ritchie, H. & Roser, M. Mobile Phone Adoption. *Our World
    Data* (2017).

38. Horace Dedieu. Asymco Technology Adoption Dataset.
    (2018).

39. Meadows, D. H. & Club of Rome. *The Limits to growth; a report
    for the Club of Rome's project on the predicament of mankind*.
    (Universe Books, 1972).

40. Seba, T. & Arbib, J. *Rethinking Humanity: Five Foundational Sector
    Disruptions, the Lifecycle of Civilizations, and the Coming Age of
    Freedom*. (Tony Seba, 2020).

41.   Rogers, E. M. *Diffusion of innovations.* (Free Press of Glencoe, 1962).

42.   Geroski, P. A. Models of technology diffusion. *Res. Policy* 29, 603–625 (2000).

43.   Ritchie, H. & Roser, M. Technology Adoption in US Households. *Our World Data* (2017).

44.   California Energy Commission. Energy Commission Adopts Standards Requiring Solar Systems for New Homes, First in Nation. *California Energy Commission* (2018).

45.   Green, M. Banks worth $47 trillion adopt new U.N.-backed climate principles. *Reuters* https://www.reuters.com/article/us-climate-change-un-banks/banks-worth-47-trillion-adopt-new-u-n-backed-climate-principles-idUSKBN1W70QO (2019).

46.   The Guardian staff. Labour party pledges to ban sale of non-electric cars by 2030. *The Observer* (2019).

47.   Lloyd, S. Ultimate physical limits to computation. *Nature* 406, 1047–1054 (2000).

48.   Our World in Data, Ritchie, H. & Roser, M. Emissions by sector. *Our World in Data* https://ourworldindata.org/emissions-by-sector (2020).

49.   Arbib, J. & Seba, T. *Rethinking Transportation 2020-2030.* (2017).

50.   Seba, T. & Tubb, C. *Rethinking Food and Agriculture 2020-2030.* https://www.rethinkx.com/food-and-agriculture (2019).

51.   Dorr, A. & Seba, T. *Rethinking Energy 2020-2030: Solar, Wind, and Batteries is Just the Beginning.* www.rethinkx.com/energy (2020).

52. Dirksen, N. *et al.* Learned control of urinary reflexes in cattle to help reduce greenhouse gas emissions. *Curr. Biol.* 31, R1033–R1034 (2021).

53. Cairns, R. This dairy-tech startup has created a step counter for cows. *CNN* https://www.cnn.com/2022/02/02/business/stellapps-india-dairy-hnk-spc-intl/index.html (2022).

54. Dorr, A. The impact pulse and restoration curves: Going beyond mitigation and stabilization. *Anthropocene* 16, 61–66 (2016).

55. IPCC. *Climate Change 2014: Synthesis Report Contribution of Working Groups I, II and III to the Fifth Assessment Report of the Intergovernmental Panel on Climate Change.* 151 (2014).

56. IPCC. *AR6 Climate Change 2021: The Physical Science Basis.* https://www.ipcc.ch/report/ar6/wg1 (2021).

57. van Vuuren, D. P. *et al.* The representative concentration pathways: an overview. *Clim. Change* 109, 5 (2011).

58. van Vuuren, D. P. *et al.* RCP2.6: exploring the possibility to keep global mean temperature increase below 2°C. *Clim. Change* 109, 95 (2011).

59. Pachauri, R. K. *et al. Climate Change 2014: Synthesis Report. Contribution of Working Groups I, II and III to the Fifth Assessment Report of the Intergovernmental Panel on Climate Change.* (IPCC, 2014).

60. Riahi, K. *et al.* The Shared Socioeconomic Pathways and their energy, land use, and greenhouse gas emissions implications: An overview. *Glob. Environ. Change* 42, 153–168 (2017).

61. Kriegler, E. *et al.* Fossil-fueled development (SSP5): An energy and resource intensive scenario for the 21st century. *Glob. Environ. Change* 42, 297–315 (2017).

62. IRENA. *Renewable Capacity Statistics 2021*.
     https://www.irena.org/publications/2021/March/Renewable
     -Capacity-Statistics-2021 (2021).

63. NREL. *2012 Renewable Energy Data Book*.
     https://www.nrel.gov/docs/fy14osti/60197.pdf (2012).

64. U.S. EIA. Electric Power Monthly. *U.S. Energy Information
     Administration*
     https://www.eia.gov/electricity/monthly/epm_table_grapher.
     php?t=table_es1b (2022).

65. Global100REStrategyGroup.org.
     Global100REStrategyGroup.org. *Joint declaration of the global
     100% renewable energy strategy group*
     https://global100restrategygroup.org/ (2022).

66. U.S. EPA. Greenhouse Gas Inventory Data Explorer | US
     EPA. *U.S. Environmental Protection Agency*
     https://cfpub.epa.gov/ghgdata/inventoryexplorer/#allsectors
     /allgas/econsect/current (2019).

67. Our World in Data. Cars, planes, trains: where do CO2
     emissions from transport come from? *Our World in Data*
     https://ourworldindata.org/co2-emissions-from-transport
     (2020).

68. UNCTAD. *Review of Maritime Transport 2021*.
     https://unctad.org/system/files/official-
     document/rmt2021_en_0.pdf (2021).

69. Hayek, M. N., Harwatt, H., Ripple, W. J. & Mueller, N. D. The
     carbon opportunity cost of animal-sourced food production
     on land. *Nat. Sustain.* 4, 21–24 (2021).

70. FAO. *The State of World Fisheries and Aquaculture 2020:
     Sustainability in action*. (FAO, 2020). doi:10.4060/ca9229en.

71. Costello, C. *et al.* Global fishery prospects under contrasting management regimes. *Proc. Natl. Acad. Sci. U. S. A.* 113, 5125–5129 (2016).

72. National Academies of Sciences, Engineering, and Medicine. *Negative Emissions Technologies and Reliable Sequestration: A Research Agenda.* (The National Academies Press, 2019). doi:10.17226/25259.

73. Bach, L. T., Gill, S. J., Rickaby, R. E. M., Gore, S. & Renforth, P. CO_2 Removal With Enhanced Weathering and Ocean Alkalinity Enhancement: Potential Risks and Co-benefits for Marine Pelagic Ecosystems. *Front. Clim.* 1, (2019).

74. Montserrat, F. *et al.* Olivine Dissolution in Seawater: Implications for CO_2 Sequestration through Enhanced Weathering in Coastal Environments. *Environ. Sci. Technol.* 51, 3960–3972 (2017).

75. Ritchie, H. & Roser, M. Meat and Dairy Production. *Our World Data* (2017).

76. Ritchie, H. If the world adopted a plant-based diet we would reduce global agricultural land use from 4 to 1 billion hectares. *Our World in Data* https://ourworldindata.org/land-use-diets (2021).

77. Grove, R. The origins of environmentalism. *Nature* 345, 11–14 (1990).

78. Clayton, J. *Natural Rivals: John Muir, Gifford Pinchot, and the Creation of America's Public Lands.* (Pegasus Books, 2019).

79. Society for Ecological Restoration. The Science and Practice of Ecological Restoration Book Series - Society for Ecological Restoration. https://www.ser.org/page/IPBookTitles/The-Science-and-Practice-of-Ecological-Restoration.htm (2022).

80. Palmer, M. A., Zedler, J. B., Falk, D. A. & PhD, D. K. H. *Foundations of Restoration Ecology.* (Island Press, 2016).

81.   PhD, D. K. H. *Primer of Ecological Restoration.* (Island Press, 2020).

82.   Galatowitsch, S. M. *Ecological Restoration.* (Sinauer Associates is an imprint of Oxford University Press, 2012).

83.   Alder, J., Campbell, B., Karpouzi, V., Kaschner, K. & Pauly, D. Forage Fish: From Ecosystems to Markets. *Annu. Rev. Environ. Resour.* 33, 153–166 (2008).

84.   Alternative protein company database (2022) | GFI. https://gfi.org/resource/alternative-protein-company-database/ (2022).

85.   Duarte, C. M. *et al.* Rebuilding marine life. *Nature* 580, 39–51 (2020).

86.   Lagi, M., Bertrand, K. Z. & Bar-Yam, Y. *The Food Crises and Political Instability in North Africa and the Middle East.* https://papers.ssrn.com/abstract=1910031 (2011) doi:10.2139/ssrn.1910031.

87.   United States Holocaust Memorial Museum. Great Depression. *Holocaust Encyclopedia* https://encyclopedia.ushmm.org/content/en/article/the-great-depression (2022).

88.   Westlake, K. *Landfill Waste Pollution and Control.* (Woodhead Publishing, 2014).

89.   Cheremisinoff, N. Handbook of Pollution Prevention Practices. *Routledge & CRC Press* https://www.routledge.com/Handbook-of-Pollution-Prevention-Practices/Cheremisinoff/p/book/9780367578817.

90.   Cheremisinoff, N. *Handbook of Solid Waste Management and Waste Minimization Technologies.* (Butterworth-Heinemann, 2003).

91. *Sustainable Environmental Clean-up - 1st Edition.* (Elsevier, 2021).

92. *Environmental Waste Management.* (Routledge, 2020).

93. Senko, J. F., Peckham, S. H., Aguilar-Ramirez, D. & Wang, J. H. Net illumination reduces fisheries bycatch, maintains catch value, and increases operational efficiency. *Curr. Biol.* 32, 911-918.e2 (2022).

94. Roque, B. M., Salwen, J. K., Kinley, R. & Kebreab, E. Inclusion of Asparagopsis armata in lactating dairy cows' diet reduces enteric methane emission by over 50 percent. *J. Clean. Prod.* 234, 132–138 (2019).

95. Williams, E. L., Bartone, S. A., Swanson, E. K. & Stokes, L. C. The American electric utility industry's role in promoting climate denial, doubt, and delay. *Environ. Res. Lett.* 17, 094026 (2022).

96. IEA. Lighting – Analysis. *IEA* https://www.iea.org/reports/lighting (2021).

97. Christensen, C. M. The Innovator's Dilemma: When New Technologies Cause Great Firms to Fail. (1997).

98. Dorr, A. Common errors in reasoning about the future: Three informal fallacies. *Technol. Forecast. Soc. Change* 116, 322–330 (2017).

99. Martinez-Alier, J. *The Environmentalism of the Poor: A Study of Ecological Conflicts and Valuation.* (Edward Elgar Publishing, 2003).

100. *Liberation Ecologies: Environment, Development, Social Movements.* (Routledge, 1996).

101. Browder, K. C. *et al.* In vivo partial reprogramming alters age-associated molecular changes during physiological aging in mice. *Nat. Aging* 2, 243–253 (2022).

102. Salk News. Cellular rejuvenation therapy safely reverses signs
     of aging in mice. *Salk Institute for Biological Studies*
     https://www.salk.edu/news-release/cellular-rejuvenation-
     therapy-safely-reverses-signs-of-aging-in-mice/ (2022).

103. Hirsch, R. E. *De-Extinction: The Science of Bringing Lost Species
     Back to Life.*

104. O'Connor, M. R. *Resurrection Science: Conservation, De-Extinction
     and the Precarious Future of Wild Things.*

105. Shapiro, B. *How to Clone a Mammoth: The Science of De-Extinction.*
     (Princeton University Press, 2020).

106. The Frozen Ark. The Frozen Ark. *The Frozen Ark*
     https://www.frozenark.org (2022).

107. San Diego Zoo. Frozen Zoo. *San Diego Zoo Wildlife Alliance*
     https://science.sandiegozoo.org/resources/frozen-
     zoo%C2%AE (2016).

108. Harrabin, R. Artificial lightning zaps farm stink. *BBC News*
     (2021).

109. Garrison, C. & Hernandez, L. Fish waste become octopus
     food as farms expand amid captivity concerns. *Reuters* (2022).

110. Wipulasena, A. & Mashal, M. Sri Lanka's Plunge Into Organic
     Farming Brings Disaster. *The New York Times* (2021).

111. Wilson, E. O. *Biophilia.* (Harvard University Press, 1984).

112. Leopold, A. *Round River: From the Journals of Aldo Leopold.*
     (Oxford University Press, 1953).

113. Sessions, G. *Deep Ecology for the Twenty-First Century: Readings on
     the Philosophy and Practice of the New Environmentalism.*
     (Shambhala, 1995).

114. Devall, B. & Sessions, G. *Deep Ecology.* (Gibbs Smith, 1985).

115. Smith, M. B. The Value of A Tree: Public Debates of John Muir and Gifford Pinchot. *Historian* 60, 757–778 (1998).

116. The Proactionary Principle: Optimizing Technological Outcomes. in *The Transhumanist Reader: Classical and Contemporary Essays on the Science, Technology, and Philosophy of the Human Future* (eds. More, M. & Vita-More, N.) (Wiley-Blackwell, 2013).

INDEX

ABOUT THE AUTHOR

 **Adam Dorr** is the Director of Research at the independent think tank RethinkX. His team's work has had a substantial impact on global policymaking, investment, and public understanding around new technologies in the energy, transportation, and food sectors. He is an environmental social scientist and technology theorist whose publications have focused on understanding the dynamics of the energy, transportation, and food disruptions and their implications for climate change. Adam is a passionate advocate for optimism and progress, and regularly presents on stage, radio, podcasts, and television. He completed his MS at the University of Michigan's School for the Environment and Sustainability and his PhD at UCLA's Luskin School of Public Affairs.

RethinkX is a philanthropically-funded nonpartisan think tank founded by renowned technology thought leader and entrepreneur Tony Seba together with technology investor and philanthropist James Arbib. The mission of RethinkX is to facilitate a robust global conversation about the threats and opportunities of technology-driven disruptions, and to highlight choices for a more equitable, healthy, resilient, and stable future. To that end, RethinkX analyzes and forecasts disruptions and their implications in order to help policymakers, civic leaders, investors, and the public make better-informed decisions.

Learn more at adamdorr.com and rethinkx.com.

Disclaimer

All opinions and views expressed by the author in this Book Content are solely those of the author and do not reflect the opinions or views of RethinkX or its respective affiliates.

The author has made every effort to ensure the accuracy of the information in this Book Content was correct at time of publication. RethinkX and the author disclaim any and all liability to any party for any direct, indirect, implied, punitive, special, incidental or other consequential damages arising directly or indirectly from any use of the Book Content, which is provided as-is, and without warranties.

The information provided in this book is for informational purposes only and is not intended to be a source of investment advice or credit analysis with respect to the material presented. The information and/or documents contained in this book do not constitute legal or financial advice. You should not rely upon the material or information in this book as a basis for making any business, legal, or other decisions. The publisher and the author do not make any guarantee or other promise as to any results that may be obtained from using the content of this book.

Printed in Great Britain
by Amazon

22175538R00142